Foundation
GCSE Mathematics
Revision and Practice

Homework Book

David Rayner

OXFORD

UNIVERSITY PRESS

Great Clarendon Street, Oxford OX2 6DP

Oxford University Press is a department of the University of Oxford.
It furthers the University's objective of excellence in research, scholarship,
and education by publishing worldwide in

Oxford New York

Auckland Cape Town Dar es Salaam Hong Kong Karachi
Kuala Lumpur Madrid Melbourne Mexico City Nairobi
New Delhi Shanghai Taipei Toronto

With offices in

Argentina Austria Brazil Chile Czech Republic France Greece
Guatemala Hungary Italy Japan South Korea Poland Portugal
Singapore Switzerland Thailand Turkey Ukraine Vietnam

Oxford is a registered trade mark of Oxford University Press
in the UK and in certain other countries

British Library Cataloguing in Publication Data

Data available

ISBN 0 19 915139 3

ISBN 978 019 9151394

10 9 8 7 6 5 4 3 2

Printed and bound in Great Britain by Bell and Bain Ltd; Glasgow

Acknowledgements

The image on the cover is reproduced courtesy of Wire Design/Digital Vision.

1   Number 1

Homework 1A

1.1 pages 1–3

1 Copy and complete.

   a $724 = 700 + \square + 4$

   b $916 = \square + 10 + 6$

   c $2537 = \square + \square + \square + 7$

2 Write these numbers in words.

   a 715   **b** 8610   **c** 26 400

3 Write these numbers in order of size, smallest first.

   a 416, 307, 317, 49, 311

   b 25 000, twelve thousand, 15 555, 9900

   c 724, 707, 763, 719, 79

4 Take 200 away from

   a 615   **b** 8720   **c** 422

5 Add 300 on to

   a 267   **b** 6114   **c** 8099

6 a Use these cards to make the largest possible 3-figure number.

   b What is the smallest 3-figure number you can make?

   c Use two of the cards to make the smallest possible 2-figure number.

             2   7   6

7 Write the number that is one thousand more than

   a 614   **b** 2850

   c 23 644   **d** 19 600

8 Write the number that is ten more than

   a 3784   **b** 4089

   c 1111   **d** 294

9 Write in figures the number 'two hundred and ten thousand, six hundred and ten'.

10 a Use these cards to make the largest possible 4-figure number.

   b Use all four cards to make the smallest possible 4-figure number. (You cannot start with zero.)

             4   0   8   3

Homework 1B●

1.1 pages 4–6

1 The **factors** of 8 are 1, 2, 4, 8 (the numbers that divide into 8 exactly). Write the factors of these numbers.

   a 6   **b** 15   **c** 9   **d** 18   **e** 21   **f** 36   **g** 28   **h** 40

2 Copy and complete these tables.

  a

Number	Factors	Common factors
8		
12		

  b

Number	Factors	Common factors
25		
40		

3 The first four **multiples** of 6 are 6, 12, 18, 24.
Write the first four multiples of

   a 2   **b** 5   **c** 7   **d** 11

In questions **4** to **6** find the 'odd one out'. (The number which is not a multiple of the number given.)

4 Multiples of 3: 6, 12, 20, 36

5 Multiples of 6: 6, 12, 120, 28

6 Multiples of 8: 16, 22, 40, 88

7 **a** Write the first five multiples of 3.
   b Write the first five multiples of 4.
   c Write the least common multiple (L.C.M.) of 3 and 4.
     (The L.C.M. is the lowest number that is in both lists.)

8 **a** Write the first five multiples of 4.
   b Write the first five multiples of 10.
   c Write the L.C.M. of 4 and 10.

9 **a** Write the **factors** of 15.
   b Write the factors of 25.
   c Write the highest common factor (H.C.F.) of 15 and 25.
     (The H.C.F. is the highest number that is is in both lists.)

10 From these five numbers
   3   6   10   15   40
   choose
   a the number that is a multiple of 8
   b the two numbers that are factors of 24
   c the number that is a multiple of 20.

Homework 1CⒺ

1.1 pages 7–12

1 Which of these numbers are prime numbers?

   3   4   5   6   7   19   20

2 Copy this statement and write 'true' or 'false'.

'There is only one even prime number.'

3 Copy and complete this list of the first seven square numbers.

$1, 4, 9, \square, \square, \square, \square$

4 Evaluate these.

  a 5^2 **b** 10^2 **c** $1^2 + 9^2$ **d** $3^2 + 4^2$

5 Write the value of

  a $\sqrt{16}$ **b** $\sqrt{36}$ **c** $\sqrt{1}$ **d** $5 + \sqrt{49}$

6 a Write the smallest square number that is greater than 100.

  b Is the number in part **a** a prime number?

7 Answer 'true' or 'false'.

  a $3 \times 3 \times 3 = 27$, so 27 is a cube number

  b $1^3 + 2^3 + 3^3 = 18$

  c There are no prime numbers that are also cube numbers.

  d $4^2 + \sqrt{4} = 10$

8 Write the number from each list that is **not** a prime number.

  a 5, 15, 23, 29   **b** 2, 11, 17, 27   **c** 31, 37, 41, 49

9 Find the number.

a	A 2-digit number A prime number The sum of its digits is 8

b	A 2-digit number A multiple of 9 Divisible by 7

c	A factor of 60 A square number

d	A multiple of 3 A cube number A 2-digit number

10 From these four numbers

  8   18   61   64

choose

  a the number that is a cube number but not a square number

  b the numbers that are cube numbers

  c the number that is prime

  d the number that is one less than a prime number

  e the two numbers that add up to give a cube number.

Homework 1D C

1.2 pages 13–14

Copy and complete.

1　　3 8
　　+ 4 2
　　―――

2　　2 7 3
　　+ 1 8 4
　　―――

3　　4 0 6 5
　　+ 1 2 3 5
　　―――

4　　9 6
　　− 1 8
　　―――

5　　2 3 7
　　− 1 5 4
　　―――

6　　6 0 9
　　− 3 3 9
　　―――

7　　4 1 2 3
　　− 2 0 6 1
　　―――

8　　2 6 5 5
　　+ 8 2 4 5
　　―――

9　　　9 1 6 0
　　+ 1 2 2 7 5
　　―――

10　　5 2 1 9
　　− 2 5 7 0
　　―――

11 Alan's car had a mileage of 27 114. In the next year
he drove a further 8754 miles. What was the new mileage?

12 Sam has £2455 in her bank account. She writes a cheque
for £630. How much is there now in the account?

13 Priya's father is 178 cm tall. Priya is 19 cm shorter.
  a How tall is Priya?
  b Priya's brother is 22 cm taller than she is. How tall is Priya's
  brother?

Homework 1E C

1.2 pages 15–16

Copy and complete.

1　　3 2
　　×　 4
　　―――

2　　2 5
　　×　 3
　　―――

3　　8 4
　　×　 4
　　―――

4　　7 0
　　×　 6
　　―――

5　　9 0 1
　　×　　 9
　　―――

6 3) 945　　**7** 5) 310　　**8** 6) 342　　**9** 5) 175　　**10** 7) 1568

11 a How many hours are there in a day?
  b How many hours are there in a week?

12 Jake divides £189 equally between seven people. How much does
each person receive?

13 a Alan buys 9 litres of petrol at 96p per litre. How much does it cost?
  b What change does he receive from £10?

14 Multiply the sum of the numbers 376 and 289 by the difference
between the numbers 104 and 95.

Homework 1F⊖

1.2 pages 13–17

Make two copies of this crossnumber pattern and then fill in the answers using the clues.

A

Across	Down
1 $17 + 9$	**1** $99 + 141$
2 $25 + 59$	**3** $835 - 213$
4 $132 + 316$	**5** $6 + 37 + 802$
6 $400 - 48$	**9** $1234 - 318$
7 $85 - 36$	**10** $87 + 34$
8 $15 + 47$	**11** $211 - 79$
9 $200 - 105$	**12** $1385 - 905$
11 $400 - 389$	**13** $15 + 16 + 35$
12 $12 + 13 + 17$	**16** $222 - 183$
14 $82 - 46$	
15 $4922 + 3214$	
17 $72 + 24 - 36$	

B

Across	Down
1 $1000 \div 40$	**1** $(6 \times 40) + 3$
2 $111 - 22$	**3** $610 - 38$
4 $2562 \div 6$	**5** $3 \times 5 \times 5 \times 10$
6 $(40 \times 12) - 53$	**9** $6 \times 6 \times 6$
7 $310 - 251$	**10** $7 \times 7 \times 7$
8 $736 \div 8$	**11** 11×79
9 $1000 \div 50$	**12** $7 + 84 + 736$
11 $(8 \times 8) + 17$	**13** $(29 - 4) \times 3$
12 $3 \times 4 \times 7$	**16** $(5 \times 6) - 13$
14 22×3	
15 $11\,575 \div 5$	
17 $4013 - 3956$	

Homework 1G⊖

1.2 pages 19–20

Copy the sums and find the missing digits.

1 a
```
    1  5  6
 + ☐  2  3
 ─────────
    8 ☐ ☐
```

b
```
    5  6 ☐
 + ☐  3  5
 ─────────
    7 ☐  8
```

c
```
   ☐  6  1
 + 2  6 ☐
 ─────────
   8 ☐  0
```

2 a
```
    7  4  6
 + 1 ☐  2
 ─────────
   ☐  7 ☐
```

b
```
    3 ☐  5
 + 4  4  8
 ─────────
   ☐  9 ☐
```

c
```
    5  6  6
 + ☐  6 ☐
 ─────────
    9 ☐  1
```

3 a
```
        5 □
    ×     4
    ───────
    2 2 4
```

b
```
        6 □
    ×     6
    ───────
    3 9 0
```

c
```
      □ □ 6
    ×     7
    ───────
    2 2 8 2
```

4 a □□□ ÷ 3 = 50   **b** □□ × 4 = 112

  c 8 × □ = 72   **d** □□□ ÷ 6 = 36

5 a
```
    7 □ 3
  + 1 6 □
  ───────
  □ 9 0
```

b
```
    6 □ 5
  + □ 6 □
  ───────
  9 2 8
```

c
```
    □ 4 □
  + 2 □ 7
  ───────
  6 7 1
```

6 a □□ × 8 = 280   **b** □□ × 10 = 73□

  c 56 ÷ □ = 28   **d** □□□ ÷ 9 = 32

Homework 1H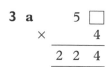

1.3 pages 21–25

1 What part of each shape is shaded? Write each answer as a fraction and as a decimal.

a

b

c

2 Write each fraction as a decimal.

  a $\dfrac{7}{10}$ **b** $\dfrac{27}{100}$ **c** $\dfrac{6}{100}$ **d** $\dfrac{84}{100}$ **e** $\dfrac{2}{100}$

3 Write each sequence and find the next two terms.

  a 0·5   0·6   0·7   ___   ___
  b 0·1   0·3   0·5   0·7   ___   ___
  c 1·1   1·4   1·7   2·0   ___   ___

4 Write each list of numbers in order, smallest first.

  a 0·71   0·7   0·814
  b 95   94·9   92·56
  c 11   10·8   11·02   10·85
  d 0·41   4·1   3·95   0·402
  e 0·35   0·5   0·405   0·36

5 Increase each number by $\dfrac{1}{10}$.

  a 17·24   **b** 8·02   **c** 123·9   **d** 11·671

6 Copy each statement and write 'true' or 'false'.

  a 0·8 = 0·80   **b** 3·1 > 3   **c** 0·6 > 0·7   **d** 0·7 = $\dfrac{7}{10}$

  e 3·14 = 3·41   **f** 0·26 = 0·2600   **g** 0·01 > 0·001   **h** 0·1 + 0·1 = 0·2

7 Write the value indicated by the arrow on each scale.

a 0 ⌊ᴜᴜᴜᴜᴜᴜᴜᴜ⌋ 1

b 10 ⌊ᴜᴜᴜᴜᴜᴜᴜᴜ⌋ 11

c 3 ⌊ᴜᴜᴜᴜᴜᴜᴜᴜ⌋ 4

d 0 ⌊ᴜᴜᴜᴜᴜᴜᴜᴜ⌋ 10

e 0 ⌊ᴜᴜᴜᴜᴜᴜᴜᴜ⌋ 50

f 7 ⌊ᴜᴜᴜᴜᴜᴜᴜᴜ⌋ 8

g 8 ⌊ᴜᴜᴜᴜᴜᴜᴜᴜ⌋ 10

h 2 ⌊ᴜᴜᴜᴜᴜᴜᴜᴜ⌋ 2·1

i 0 ⌊ᴜᴜᴜᴜᴜᴜᴜᴜ⌋ 1

Homework 1I **C**

1.3 pages 25–27

Copy and complete.

1	**2**	**3**	**4**	**5**
3·2	8·2	3·5	0·52	35·6
+1·6	+1·9	+0·44	+3·7	+ 3·9

6	**7**	**8**	**9**	**10**
9·7	9·3	6·2	1·45	3·34
−6·5	−4·5	−1·7	+1·2	−1·84

11 The normal price of a radio is £27·90. In a sale its price was £18·95. How much cheaper was the radio during the sale?

12 Jan spends £15·19 on petrol, £7·25 at the off-licence and £11·50 at the supermarket. How much does she spend altogether?

13 Annie spent 95p on a pen, £18·60 on shoes and £2·47 on food.
   a How much did she spend altogether?
   b How much was left from the £25 she started with?

14 Work out.
   a 15·4 − 9
   b 8·76 − 5
   c 254·3 − 240
   d 8 − 5·4
   e 16 − 8·7
   f 12 − 9·7
   g 7 − 3·25
   h 4·24 + 7 − 4·01
   i 3·5 + 8 − 2·16

15 Find the totals.
   a £1·55 + £1·45 + 55p
   b £2·40 + £2·25 + 28p
   c £12 + £5·50 + 45p + 5p
   d £5·70 − 50p
   e £5 − 75p
   f £0·75 + 70p + £4 + 4p

Homework 1J C

1.3 pages 27–29

Work out.

1 $3\cdot24 \times 10$	**2** $0\cdot156 \times 100$	**3** $3\cdot4 \times 100$	**4** $0\cdot814 \times 100$
5 $75\cdot6 \div 10$	**6** $907\cdot4 \div 10$	**7** $86 \div 10$	**8** $476\cdot5 \div 1000$
9 17×100	**10** $0\cdot13 \times 1000$	**11** $217 \div 100$	**12** $0\cdot07 \times 10$
13 $589 \div 1000$	**14** $0\cdot07 \times 10\,000$	**15** $0\cdot04 \div 10$	**16** $200\cdot8 \div 100$

17 A shop manager buys 100 CDs at £4·55 each. What is the total cost?

18 100 people share a lottery prize of £36 500. How much does each person receive?

Work out.

19 $7\cdot4 \times 3$	**20** $8\cdot2 \times 5$	**21** $19\cdot51 \times 2$	**22** $14\cdot6 \times 10$
23 $19\cdot7 \times 8$	**24** $64\cdot85 \times 4$	**25** $0\cdot71 \times 100$	**26** $282\cdot4 \times 7$

27 Find the cost of 5 jars of jam at £1·25 each.

28 Find the total cost of 4 tins of peaches at £1·30 each and 2 bottles of olive oil at £4·65 each.

29 Find the total cost.

    a 2 jars at £1·75 each
       4 boxes at £0·40 each
       1 bottle at £1·25

    b 6 tins at £0·75 each
       3 bags at £0·69 each
       4 packets at 21p each

    c 12 eggs at 45p per dozen
       7 bottles at £0·37 each
       3 oranges at 10p each

    d 3 loaves at 42p each
       2 cauliflowers at 45p each
       4 cans at £1·50 each

Homework 1K C

1.3 pages 29–30

Do these multiplications.

1 $0\cdot7 \times 0\cdot2$	**2** $0\cdot5 \times 0\cdot6$	**3** $0\cdot8 \times 5$	**4** $4\cdot2 \times 0\cdot4$
5 $15\cdot2 \times 0\cdot2$	**6** $28\cdot4 \times 0\cdot7$	**7** $6\cdot4 \times 0\cdot01$	**8** $84\cdot6 \times 0\cdot02$

Now do these divisions.

9 $9\cdot2 \div 4$	**10** $8\cdot5 \div 5$	**11** $73\cdot8 \div 6$	**12** $45\cdot78 \div 7$
13 $0\cdot62 \div 5$	**14** $0\cdot84 \div 5$	**15** $11\cdot1 \div 10$	**16** $58\cdot5 \div 9$

17 John cuts a pie weighing 2·43 kg into 9 equal pieces. How much does each piece weigh?

18 Electric cable costs £0·60 per metre. How much will 11·5 metres of cable cost?

19 You have £83·04 to share equally between you and five other people. What will your share be?

20 Copy the crossnumber pattern and fill it in using the clues.

Across	**Down**
1 100 ÷ 4	**1** 1680 ÷ 7
2 285 ÷ 5	**3** 804 ÷ 3
4 3987 ÷ 9	**5** 1580 ÷ 5
6 1476 ÷ 6	**9** 308 ÷ 2
7 152 ÷ 8	**10** 5238 ÷ 6
8 616 ÷ 7	**11** 2358 ÷ 9
9 176 ÷ 11	**12** 3633 ÷ 7
11 175 ÷ 7	**13** 1001 ÷ 11
12 342 ÷ 6	**16** 168 ÷ 6
14 640 ÷ 10	
15 15 852 ÷ 12	
17 693 ÷ 7	

Homework 1L **C**

1.3 page 30

> **Reminder**
> Work out 9·36 ÷ 0·4. Multiply both numbers by 10 so that
> you can divide by a **whole number**.
> So you work out 93·6 ÷ 4.
> $$\begin{array}{r} 2\ 3 \cdot\ 4 \\ 4\overline{)9\,^1 3 \cdot\,^1 6} \end{array}$$
> The answer is 23·4.

Work out.

1 1·48 ÷ 0·2	**2** 2·52 ÷ 0·4	**3** 0·942 ÷ 0·3	**4** 0·712 ÷ 0·2
5 0·1368 ÷ 0·04	**6** 0·1683 ÷ 0·03	**7** 0·498 ÷ 0·06	**8** 5·04 ÷ 0·7
9 0·42 ÷ 0·03	**10** 11·7 ÷ 0·1	**11** 0·0042 ÷ 0·002	**12** 0·0561 ÷ 0·11

13 Heidi cuts a pie weighing 7·2 kg into several pieces, each weighing 0·6 kg.
How many pieces are there?

14 A rod is 2·86 m long. It is divided into 11 equal pieces. How long is
each piece?

15 A rod is 1·36 m long. It is divided into several pieces of length 0·08 m.
How many pieces are there?

16 How many times will the jug have
to be filled and emptied to completely
empty the drum?

Drum 8·4 litres   Jug 0·6 litres

17 Before eating, a bird weighs 0·31 kg. A worm weighs 8 grams.
How much will the bird weigh after eating 9 worms?

Homework 1M

1.3 page 31

These questions are a mixture of addition, subtraction, multiplication and division.

Work out.

1 $4{\cdot}21 \times 10$	**2** $0{\cdot}63 \times 1000$	**3** $5 + 4{\cdot}32$	**4** $6{\cdot}2 - 5$
5 $4{\cdot}8 \div 4$	**6** $73{\cdot}6 \div 10$	**7** $213 \div 100$	**8** $0{\cdot}0086 \times 10$
9 $0{\cdot}09 \div 9$	**10** $8{\cdot}36 \div 0{\cdot}2$	**11** $5{\cdot}2 \div 0{\cdot}04$	**12** $0{\cdot}186 \div 0{\cdot}03$

13 Write 'five pounds 40p' in figures.

14 Write 'five pounds 4p' in figures.

15 Write '1207·09' in words.

16 A builder buys wood in lengths of 5 m. How many pieces of length 75 cm can be cut from each 5 m length? How much is left over?

17 A pile of nine ceramic tiles is 4·05 cm thick. What is the thickness of each tile?

18 A newsagent buys 2000 magazines at 13·2p each and sells them all at 25p each. What is her total profit in pounds?

19 Forty-five passengers on a coach each pay a fare of £5·60.
  a How much money is raised in this way?
  b If the running costs of the coach are £145·50, how much profit does the coach owner make?

20 A pile of 600 sheets of paper is 10·44 cm thick. How thick is each sheet of paper?

21 Mr Kipling cuts a cake of weight 4·6 kg into small pieces each weighing 0·2 kg. How many pieces are there?

22 Hao spends £1·15 in the first shop and twice as much in the second shop. How much is left of the £5 he started with?

Homework 1N

1.4 pages 32–35

1 List these temperatures from the coldest to the hottest.
  a $-4\,°C, 3\,°C, -8\,°C$
  b $-5\,°C, 0\,°C, -3\,°C, -1\,°C$
  c $22\,°C, -8\,°C, -11\,°C, -2\,°C$
  d $-5\,°C, -2{\cdot}5\,°C, -3\,°C, -1\,°C$

2 Copy each sequence and find the next two numbers.
  a $9, 7, 5, 3, \_\_, \_\_$
  b $14, 10, 6, 2, \_\_, \_\_$
  c $10, 5, 0, \_\_, \_\_$
  d $-6, -4, -2, \_\_, \_\_$
  e $-8, -7, -6, \_\_, \_\_$
  f $11, 7, 3, \_\_, \_\_$

Work out.

3 $7 - 4$	**4** $4 - 7$	**5** $2 - 8$	**6** $3 - 11$
7 $-2 + 4$	**8** $-3 - 7$	**9** $-8 - 8$	**10** $-9 + 2$
11 $-4 + 9$	**12** $4 - 11$	**13** $-15 - 3$	**14** $-6 + 6$

15 $5 - 7 + 9$ **16** $3 - 11 + 10$ **17** $-8 - 6 + 2$ **18** $-4 + 5 - 6$
19 $2 + (-9)$ **20** $-3 - (-3)$ **21** $-4 + (-5)$ **22** $8 - (-7)$
23 $-2 + (-20)$ **24** $3 - (+5)$ **25** $-5 - (-7)$ **26** $-7 + (-4)$

27 Copy and complete these addition squares.

a

+	5	2	−3	−7
−4		−2		
0				
−3				
6				

b

+	−3	−1	5	−2
6				
−5			0	
−1				
3				

Homework 10 **C**

1.4 page 36

Work out.
 1 $-5 \times (+2)$ **2** $-3 \times (-2)$ **3** $-8 \times (4)$ **4** $12 \div (-2)$
 5 $-10 \div (-2)$ **6** $(-6)^2$ **7** $-1 \times (-1)$ **8** $8 \times (-2)$
 9 $-12 \div (-6)$ **10** $16 \div (-4)$ **11** $-24 \div (4)$ **12** $49 \div (-7)$
 13 $-8 \times (-7)$ **14** $-42 \times (-7)$ **15** $3 \times (-10) \times (-1)$ **16** $-4 \times (6) \times (-3)$
 17 $10 \times (-60)$ **18** $3{\cdot}2 \times (-10)$ **19** $-2{\cdot}5 \div (-10)$ **20** $100 \times (-100)$

21 Copy and complete these multiplication squares.

a

	−3	−1	5	−2	3
2					
−4			8		
1					
−5					
−1					

b

	7	−1	0	−3	5
−5					
1					5
3					
−6				18	
10					

In questions **22** to **33** you are given $a = 4$
$b = -3$
$c = -1$

Evaluate these.
22 $a + b$ **23** $a - c$ **24** bc **25** $a^2 + c^2$ **26** ab **27** $c - b$
28 $a - b$ **29** $a + b + c$ **30** $2a + 3b$ **31** $4cb$ **32** $8(a + b)$ **33** $a(b + c)$

Homework 1P Ⓒ Mixed questions involving negative numbers

1.4 pages 32–37

Reminders		
a $-3 - 4 = -7$	Use a number line.	**b** $6 - (-2) = 6 + 2 = 8$
c $-5 \times -2 = 10$		**d** $8 \div (-2) = -4$

Work out.

1 $-7 + 3$	**2** -3×4	**3** $-3 - (-4)$	**4** $8 \div (-2)$
5 $-4 \times (-4)$	**6** $-8 - 5$	**7** $4 + (-2)$	**8** -3×1
9 $6 - 12$	**10** $0 \times (-7)$	**11** $-8 - 4$	**12** $-1 \times (-8)$
13 $12 \div (-3)$	**14** $10 \times (-10)$	**15** $18 - 30$	**16** $3 - (+8)$
17 $-16 \div 8$	**18** $-7 - 4$	**19** -4×5	**20** $-8 + 13$
21 $-8 + 2$	**22** $3 \times (-3)$	**23** $8 \div (-8)$	**24** $6 - (-3)$
25 $-6 \times (-1)$	**26** -3×0	**27** $-6 + 1$	**28** $-8 - 7$
29 $-30 + 42$	**30** $-2 + (-2)$	**31** $-4 - (-8)$	**32** $-100 + (-15)$

In questions **33** to **41** the box contains either $+$, $-$, $\times$ or $\div$.
Write each statement and put the correct operation in the box.
For example, $6 \ \square \ -2 = 8$ becomes $6 \ \boxed{-} \ -2 = 8$.

33 $8 \ \square \ -3 = 5$	**34** $10 \ \square \ -2 = -20$	**35** $-12 \ \square \ -2 = 6$
36 $-4 \ \square \ -2 = 8$	**37** $-12 \ \square \ -2 = -10$	**38** $8 \ \square \ -3 = 11$
39 $-100 \ \square \ -5 = 20$	**40** $-7 \ \square \ 7 = 0$	**41** $11 \ \square \ -2 = -22$

42 Copy each statement and write 'true' or 'false'.

a $-2 > -3$	**b** $6 < (-3)^2$	**c** $6 - (-6) = 12$	**d** $0 > -2$	**e** $-3 - 3 = 6$
f $-7 < -2$	**g** $(-2)^2 = -4$	**h** $-8 + 6 + 2 = 0$	**i** $1000 \div (-10) = -100$	

Homework 1Q Ⓒ

1.5 pages 37–39

Reminder			
'BIDMAS'	**a** $30 - 6 \times 2$	**b** $7 + 2 \times 9$	**c** $(8 \div 2) - (1 \times 2)$
	$= 30 - 12$	$= 7 + 18$	$= 4 - 2$
	$= 18$	$= 25$	$= 2$

Work out these.

1 $6 \times 3 + 2$	**2** $5 + 2 \times 4$	**3** $6 + 5 \times 2$	**4** $8 + 7 \times 2$
5 $8 - 1 \times 4$	**6** $7 + 18 \div 3$	**7** $9 + 6 \div 2$	**8** $26 - 2 \times 8$
9 $20 - 3 \times 5$	**10** $11 + 8 \div 2$	**11** $5 \times 5 - 5$	**12** $16 - 30 \div 3$
13 $10 - 20 \div 4$	**14** $7 \times 7 - 2$	**15** $9 + 7 \times 3$	**16** $20 \div 10 + 20$
17 $50 - 8 \times 4$	**18** $55 - 8 \times 5$	**19** $22 - 3 \times 7$	**20** $19 + 24 \div 6$
21 $11 + 8 \div 1$	**22** $60 - 7 \times 8$	**23** $15 - 2 \times 6$	**24** $15 \div 5 - 3$
25 $30 + 15 \div 3$	**26** $9 \times 5 + 15$	**27** $40 - 3 \times 8$	**28** $12 - 36 \div 6$
29 $3 + 20 \div 2$	**30** $13 + 8 \div 8$		

Now do these.

31 $2 \times 4 + 3 \times 5$ **32** $6 \times 6 + 7 \times 5$ **33** $1 \times 6 + 7 \times 2$ **34** $2 \times 8 + 2 \times 10$

35 $3 \times 5 - 12 \div 2$ **36** $3 \times 5 - 28 \div 4$ **37** $7 \times 4 + 2 \times 2$ **38** $30 \div 3 + 5 \times 4$

39 $20 \div 2 - 3 \times 2$ **40** $8 \div 8 - 1 \times 1$ **41** $7 \times 3 + 32 \div 2$ **42** $7 \times 5 + 33 \div 3$

43 $40 \div 8 - 60 \div 12$ **44** $40 \div 8 + 6 \times 5$ **45** $4 \times 12 + 13 \times 2$ **46** $7 \times 3 - 100 \div 5$

47 $5 + 3 \times 2 - 6$ **48** $28 - 7 \times 4 + 7$ **49** $10 - 4 \times 2 + 4$ **50** $50 + 60 \div 3 - 15$

Questions **51** to **72** involve brackets.

51 $6 + (3 \times 2) + 1$ **52** $4 \times (4 - 2) + 7$ **53** $8 + (8 - 3) \times 3$ **54** $6 \times 6 - (3 \times 3)$

55 $(10 - 1) \times 2 - 3$ **56** $8 \times (10 \div 2) - 12$ **57** $7 + 3 \times (6 \times 5)$ **58** $(3 \times 3) + 2 \times 4$

59 $8 - (3 \times 2) \div 6$ **60** $5 \times (8 - 3) - 20$ **61** $20 + 16 \div (4 \times 2)$ **62** $12 + 8 \div (8 \div 4)$

63 $(5 - 2) \times 3 + 11$ **64** $3 \times (12 - 7) + 8$ **65** $15 \div (9 - 6) + 8$ **66** $5 \times (9 + 1) + 8$

67 $8 + 3 \times (3 + 4)$ **68** $85 - (15 + 45) \div 12$ **69** $8 + (7 + 2) \div 9$ **70** $6 + 16 \div (5 - 1)$

71 $(1 + 4) \times 7 - 15$ **72** $10 + 8 \times (8 - 5)$

Homework 1R **C**

1.6 pages 40–42

> **Reminder**
> 5^2 means 5×5, so $5^2 = 25$
> 2^3 means $2 \times 2 \times 2$, so $2^3 = 8$
> $\sqrt{100}$ means 'the square root of 100', $\sqrt{100} = 10$.

1 Work out without using a calculator.
   a 3^2 **b** 4^2 **c** 7^2 **d** 1^3 **e** 3^3

2 Write these using indices (powers) (for example, $3 \times 3 \times 3 \times 3 = 3^4$).
   a $5 \times 5 \times 5 \times 5 \times 5$ **b** $6 \times 6 \times 6$ **c** $7 \times 7 \times 7 \times 7 \times 7 \times 7$
   d $10 \times 10 \times 10 \times 10 \times 10 \times 10 \times 10 \times 10$ **e** Write part **d** as an ordinary number.

3 Work out.
   a $3^2 + 2^2$ **b** $1^3 + 2^3 + 3^3$ **c** $10^2 - 9^2$

4 What number do you multiply by itself to get
   a 36   **b** 64   **c** 81?

5 Write the value of
   a $\sqrt{25}$ **b** $\sqrt{49}$ **c** $\sqrt{1}$ **d** $\sqrt{10\,000}$

6 This square picture has an area of $20\,\text{cm}^2$.
Use a calculator to find the length of each
side of the square, correct to the
nearest mm.

Homework 1S Ⓔ

1.6 pages 43–45

> **Reminders**
>
> 3^{-1} means $\frac{1}{3}$ 5^{-2} means $\frac{1}{5^2}$ $2^3 \times 2^7 = 2^{10}$ Add the indices.

In questions **1** to **5** write the numbers as fractions.

1 2^{-1} **2** 4^{-1} **3** 3^{-2} **4** 10^{-1} **5** 6^{-2}

Write in a simpler form.

6 $3^2 \times 3^3$ **7** $5^3 \times 5^4$ **8** $6^1 \times 6^6$ **9** $2^8 \times 2^3$ **10** $2^{10} \div 2^2$ **11** $3^7 \div 3^3$

12 $5^8 \div 5^2$ **13** $6^8 \div 6$ **14** $4^5 \times 4^{-1}$ **15** $7^{-2} \times 7^4$ **16** $8^7 \times 8^{-6}$ **17** $9^{-2} \times 9^{-2}$

In questions **18** to **25** copy the statements and write 'true' or 'false'.

18 $2^3 = 6$ **19** $4^3 = 64$ **20** $10^{-1} = 0{\cdot}1$ **21** $3^2 \times 3^4 = 3^6$

22 $10^{-2} = \frac{1}{100}$ **23** $5^{-2} = \frac{1}{10}$ **24** $1^3 > 3^1$ **25** $8^0 = 1$

Solve the equations to find x.

26 $2^x = 8$ **27** $4^x = 16$ **28** $10^x = 10\,000$ **29** $2^x = \frac{1}{4}$

30 Puzzle

I am thinking of a three-digit number.
It is an odd number less than 200.
The product of the digits is 4.
What number is it?

'Product of digits' means 'multiply the digits'.

Homework 1T Ⓒ Using a calculator

1.7 pages 45–49

> Use the brackets keys to work out $7{\cdot}23 - \dfrac{1{\cdot}2}{1{\cdot}53}$.
>
>
>
> The answer is $6{\cdot}446$ to 4 sf.

Work out, correct to four significant figures.

1 $85{\cdot}3 \times 21{\cdot}7$ **2** $18{\cdot}6 \div 2{\cdot}7$ **3** $10{\cdot}074 \div 8{\cdot}3$ **4** $0{\cdot}112 \times 3{\cdot}74$

5 $8 - 0{\cdot}11111$ **6** $19 + 0{\cdot}3456$ **7** $0{\cdot}841 \div 17$ **8** $11{\cdot}02 \times 20{\cdot}1$

9 $18{\cdot}3 \div 0{\cdot}751$ **10** $0{\cdot}982 \times 6{\cdot}74$ **11** $\dfrac{8{\cdot}3 + 2{\cdot}94}{3{\cdot}4}$ **12** $\dfrac{6{\cdot}1 - 4{\cdot}35}{0{\cdot}76}$

13 $\dfrac{19{\cdot}7 + 21{\cdot}4}{0{\cdot}985}$ **14** $7{\cdot}3 + \left(\dfrac{8{\cdot}2}{9{\cdot}5}\right)$ **15** $\left(\dfrac{6{\cdot}04}{18{\cdot}7}\right) - 0{\cdot}214$ **16** $\dfrac{2{\cdot}4 \times 0{\cdot}871}{4{\cdot}18}$

17 $19{\cdot}3 + \left(\dfrac{2{\cdot}6}{1{\cdot}95}\right)$ **18** $6{\cdot}41 + \dfrac{9{\cdot}58}{2{\cdot}6}$ **19** $\dfrac{19{\cdot}3 \times 0{\cdot}221}{0{\cdot}689}$ **20** $8{\cdot}3 + \dfrac{0{\cdot}64}{0{\cdot}325}$

21 $2.4 + (9.7 \times 0.642)$ **22** $11.2 + (9.75 \times 1.11)$ **23** $0.325 + \dfrac{8.6}{11.2}$ **24** $8.35^2 - 25$

25 $6.71^2 + 0.64$ **26** $3.45^3 + 11.8$ **27** $2.93^3 - 2.641$ **28** $\dfrac{7.2^2 - 4.5}{8.64}$

29 $\dfrac{13.9 + 2.97^2}{4.31}$ **30** $(3.3 - 2.84)^2$ **31** $\dfrac{(12.9 - 8.45)^2}{4.3}$ **32** $\left(\dfrac{4.4 + 6.23}{9.9}\right)^2$

33 $\dfrac{5.89}{7 - 3.83}$ **34** $\dfrac{102}{58.1 \times 65.32}$ **35** $\dfrac{18.8}{3.72 \times 1.86}$ **36** $\dfrac{904}{65.3 \times 2.86}$

37 $12.2 - \left(\dfrac{2.6}{1.95}\right)$ **38** $8.047 - \left(\dfrac{6.34}{10.2}\right)$ **39** $14.2 - \left(\dfrac{1.7}{2.4}\right)$ **40** $\dfrac{9.75 - 8.792}{4.31 - 3.014}$

Homework 1U Ⓔ Mixed questions

1.8 pages 50–58

1 By how much is a half of 72 greater than 27?

2 The first prime number is 2. What is the 7th prime number?

3 Find the missing digits.

a
```
    3 □ 5
  + □ 2 □
  ───────
    9 8 7
```
b
```
    □ 3 □
  + 4 □ 4
  ───────
    8 5 2
```
c $\square\ \square \times 5 = 60$

4 What number is a quarter of 152?

5 How many sides does a hexagon have?

6 A train is on a journey from Edinburgh to London, which is 378 miles. How much **further**, in miles, has the train to go when it has gone one-quarter of the journey?

7 Harry has a plank of wood 168 cm long.
He cuts off a piece 95 cm long.
How long is the piece that is left?

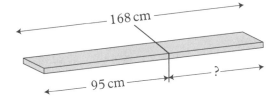

8 Copy each sequence and write the next number.
   a $7, 11, 15, 19,$ __   **b** $-2, 0, 2,$ __   **c** $3, 4, 6, 9, 13,$ __   **d** $0.7, 0.8, 0.9,$ __

9 Here is a list of numbers.
   8   15   28   29   49
   a Which number is a factor of 30?
   b Which numbers are multiples of 7?
   c Which is a square number?
   d Which is a prime number?

10 Copy the statement and write 'true' or 'false'.
   $2^{-2} = \dfrac{1}{4}$

Homework 1V

1.8 pages 50–58

1 Work out.
   a 5·6 + 13   **b** 8·2 − 3·5   **c** 18·25 − 1·7

2 If the perimeter of a square is 36 cm, what is its area?

area ?

3 Write these numbers in order, smallest first.
   a 3, 0·6, 1·7, 0·85   **b** 4, −1, 2, −7   **c** 327, 411·4, 373, 200·1

4 How many lengths of string, each 0·3 m long, can you cut from a string of length 12 m?

5 Find the distance from
   a Birmingham to Southampton
   b Sheffield to Birmingham
   c London to Plymouth.

Birmingham	London	Manchester	Sheffield	Southampton	Plymouth
120					
89	204				
87	169	37			
129	80	235	209		
203	241	287	297	149	

Distance in miles

6 **a** Write a multiple of 7 which is a square number.
   b Write a prime number which is even.
   c Write a 2-digit factor of 100.

7 Find the value of these.
   a 3^2 **b** 11^2 **c** 2^5 **d** 10^4

8 Mrs James has £1250 in her bank account. How much has she left after buying a fur coat for £415 and a carpet for £210?

9 St Stephen's Church launches an appeal for £5000.
   In the first week £540 is raised,
   in the second week £630 is raised
   and in the third week £710 is raised.
   How much more is needed to reach the target?

Target
£5000

10 **Puzzle**
   Chris is thinking of an odd number.
   It has 3 digits and the product of the digits is 2.
   It is greater than 200.
   What number is it?

Homework 1W

1.8 pages 50–58

1 Find the reading for each letter.

```
     A    B                C    D              E    F
  2  ↓    ↓ 3          400↓    ↓ 600       0·6↓    ↓  0·7
   └┴┴┴┴┴┴┴┴┘          └┴┴┴┴┴┴┴┴┘          └┴┴┴┴┴┴┴┴┘
```

2 A car park in the town centre charges 50p per car.
On Monday there were 760 cars, on Tuesday there were 815 cars
and on Wednesday there were 795 cars.
 a How many cars used the car park in the three days?
 b How much money was paid altogether for the three days?

3 Work these out, correct to 3 significant figures.

 a $4·23 - 1·71^2$ **b** $\dfrac{8·61}{4·2 - 2·95}$ **c** $\left(\dfrac{11·5}{7} - 0·9\right)^2$

4 A pound is about 0·5 kg. A young panda bear weighs 50 kg. About
how many pounds is this?

5 Twenty-four people share the cost of hiring a coach for an outing.
How much does each person pay if the total cost of the coach is £174?

6 The petrol consumption figures for two cars are shown in the
diagram.

A    B

 9 km per litre   7 km per litre

Both cars are filled up with 70 litres of petrol. Car A can go further
than car B before being filled up again. How much further?

7 In January the daily circulation of the Daily Record was four million,
two hundred and sixty thousand.
After an advertising campaign the circulation in March was four
million, seven hundred and eighty thousand.
 a What was the increase in the circulation of the paper?
 b How much **extra** money was raised each day if the price of the
   paper was 40p?

8 Mr Hansen bought celery for 55p, onions for 60p, leeks for
42p and tomatoes for 96p. How much change did he receive
from £5?

9 Use the $\boxed{x^y}$ or $\boxed{\wedge}$ button to find
 a $2·5^3$ **b** 2^8 **c** $3^4 + 4^{1·5}$

10 Work out these (remember 'BIDMAS').
 a $15 - 3 \div 3$ **b** $4^2 - 3 \times 5 - 1$ **c** $3^3 - \left(\dfrac{45}{5}\right)$

2 Algebra 1

Homework 2A ⓒ

2.1 pages 63–65

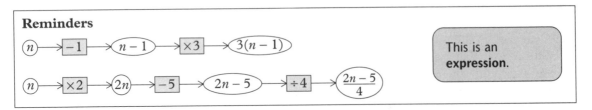

In questions **1** to **10** write the expression you obtain.

1 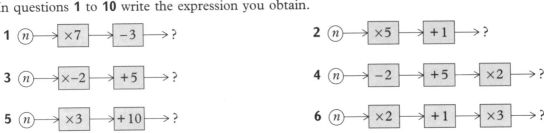 (n) → ×7 → −3 → ?

2 (n) → ×5 → +1 → ?

3 (n) → ×−2 → +5 → ?

4 (n) → −2 → +5 → ×2 → ?

5 (n) → ×3 → +10 → ?

6 (n) → ×2 → +1 → ×3 → ?

7 Start with *x* add 7 and then multiply by 4.

8 Start with *x* multiply by 4 and then add 6.

9 Start with *y*, double it, add 3 and then multiply the result by 5.

10 Start with *n*, treble it, take away 5 and then multiply the result by 7.

Draw each diagram and fill in the empty boxes.

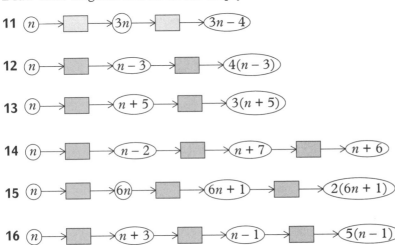

11 (n) → ☐ → (3n) → ☐ → (3n − 4)

12 (n) → ☐ → (n − 3) → ☐ → (4(n − 3))

13 (n) → ☐ → (n + 5) → ☐ → (3(n + 5))

14 (n) → ☐ → (n − 2) → ☐ → (n + 7) → ☐ → (n + 6)

15 (n) → ☐ → (6n) → ☐ → (6n + 1) → ☐ → (2(6n + 1))

16 (n) → ☐ → (n + 3) → ☐ → (n − 1) → ☐ → (5(n − 1))

In questions **17** to **20** find the resulting expression.

17 Start with x, square it and then add 7.

18 Start with x, add 10 and then square the result.

19 Start with y, double it, add 3 and then square the result.

20 Start with m, take away 5 and then multiply the result by 10.

Homework 2B●

2.1 pages 66–67

> **Reminders**
> $$2a + 5b + a - b = 3a + 4b$$
> $$6m - 3n + m - n + 5 = 7m - 4n + 5$$
>
> You can collect like terms.

Collect like terms together.

1 $5n + 6n$

2 $3x - 2x + 4x$

3 $7m + 2m - 3m$

4 $8c - 2c + c$

5 $2m + n + 3m + 6n$

6 $4n + 1 + 5n + 10$

7 $6a + 10 - 2a - 2$

8 $6h - 2y + 2h - 9y$

9 $8y - 3 + y + 9$

10 $4x - 10 - 2x + 3$

11 $x + 12y + 3x - 2y$

12 $7y + 5 + 7y - 4$

13 $3a - 2c + 5c - 2a$

14 $5x + 2y - 7y + 5x$

15 $7d - 4 + 10 - 6d$

Copy and complete.

16 $3n + \square + 2 = 8n + 2$

17 $5m + \square + 2n + \square = 6m + 10n$

18 $8a + \square + \square + 3b + 11 = 10a + 10b + 11$

19 $x^2 + 2x + \square + 3x + \square = x^2 + 8x + 7$

20 $x^2 + 8x + \square + 9x + \square = x^2 + 20x + 1$

Find the perimeter of each shape. Give your answers in their simplest form.

21
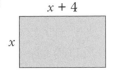
$x + 4$
x

22

x
$2x$

23
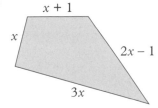
$x + 1$
x
$2x - 1$
$3x$

Homework 2C⒠

2.1 pages 66–68

Simplify these.

1 $4a + 2b + 5a + 4b$
2 $6c + 5x - 2c + 11x$
3 $5y + 7 - 3y - 4$
4 $6b - 2c + 5b - 7c$
5 $10a - 3 - 7a + 9$
6 $7c + 4a - c + 10a$
7 $8c + 5y + 10c - 4 - 8y$
8 $9a - 3 + c + 2a - 7$
9 $6d - 4a + 7d + 4a$
10 $n^2 + 5n + 3n^2 + n$
11 $3n^2 - 8n + n^2 + 8n$
12 $n^2 + 70n + 5n^2 + 6$

13 a Copy this statement and write 'true' or 'false'.
  $3 \times a \times b = 3ab$
b Write $2a \times 3b$ in a simpler form.

14 Write in a simpler form (for example $4m \times 3n = 12mn$).
  a $6a \times 2b$
  b $4n \times 3p$
  c $5n \times 6m$
  d $a \times 3n$
  e $p \times 6q$
  f $n \times 2n$
  g $3n \times 4n$
  h $6n \times 3n$
  i $7a \times 7a$

15 Find the missing lengths in these rectangles.

a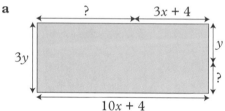

b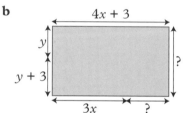

c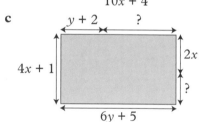

d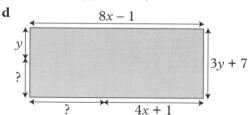

Homework 2D⒞

2.1 pages 68–69

Reminder

  $4(m + n)$ means $4 \times m + 4 \times n$
So, $4(m + n) = 4m + 4n$
Similarly, $3(2x - 4) = 6x - 12$
  $x(x + 3) = x^2 + 3x$

This is called 'removing the brackets'.

Remove the brackets.

1 $2(x + 3)$
2 $5(b - 4)$
3 $8(a - 2)$
4 $3(x + c)$
5 $7(t - y)$
6 $10(m + 1)$
7 $6(y + 2)$
8 $4(u - x)$
9 $3(x - y)$
10 $9(x - 2)$
11 $10(a + 3)$
12 $2(x + y)$
13 $4(2c + d)$
14 $5(2y - 3)$
15 $11(4d - 3h)$
16 $7(n + 2t)$
17 $n(n + 2)$
18 $n(n - 3)$
19 $n(n - 10)$
20 $x(2x + 1)$
21 $x(3x - 2)$
22 $x(4x + 1)$
23 $2x(3x + 1)$
24 $2x(x - 3)$

Remove the brackets and simplify.

25 $3(x + 2) + 4x$ **26** $5(2y - 1) - 3y$ **27** $2(4x + 1) - 7$

28 $3a + 7(2a - 3)$ **29** $10x + 3(2x - 5)$ **30** $19 + 2(5c + 7)$

31 $2(4x + 3) + 4(3x - 4)$ **32** $3(4d + 1) - 2(6d - 5)$ **33** $5a + 2(3a + 4) - 2a$

34 $9y - 5(y + 2) - 3$ **35** $11b + 3 - 3(2b - 5)$ **36** $4(a - 2) + 2(3a - 1) - 3a$

37 Here are some algebra cards.

$x + x + x$	$x^2 + x$	$x + 2$	$4x - x$
$2x + 2$	$2x$	$x^2 + 2x - x$	$2x + 1$

  a Which two cards will always give the same answer as $\boxed{3 \times x}$?

  b Which two cards will always give the same answer as $\boxed{x(x + 1)}$?

  c Which card will always give the same answer as $\boxed{2(x + 1)}$?

Homework 2E **C**

2.1 page 71

  1 Asif has n stamps
    a Frank has 10 more stamps than Asif. How many stamps does Frank have?
    b Greg has three times as many stamps as Asif. How many stamps has Greg?
    c Hank has as many stamps as Asif, Frank and Greg added together. How many stamps has Hank?

In questions **2** to **13** copy each statement and write 'true' or 'false'.

  2 $7 \times n = n \times 7$ **3** $n + n = 2n$ **4** $a + a^2 = a^3$

  5 $a \times a = a^2$ **6** $3m + 3m = 6m^2$ **7** $3 \times p \times q = 3pq$

  8 $(3m)^2 = 9m^2$ **9** $t \times t = 2t$ **10** $a \div b = b \div a$

11 $n(n - 7) = n - 7n$ **12** $5n - n = 5$ **13** $x(x + 7) = x^2 + 7x$

14 An approximate formula for changing the temperature in degrees Celsius to the temperature in degrees Fahrenheit is
    $F = 2C + 32$
    a Find F when $C = 10$.
    b Find F when $C = -15$.
    c Find the temperature in Celsius when it is $44\,°F$.

In questions **15** to **23** simplify the expressions.

15 $\dfrac{6a}{a}$ **16** $3(x + 1) - 4$ **17** $\dfrac{n \times n}{n}$

18 $a^2 + a^2 + a^2$ **19** $10e \div e$ **20** $3x(x + 1) - 3x$

21 $\dfrac{x + x + x}{x}$ **22** $\dfrac{4na}{4n}$ **23** $a(a + a)$

24 a Find an expression for the
    perimeter of the picture.
  b Find an expression for the
    area of the picture.

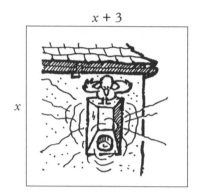

Homework 2F ⓒ

2.2 pages 72–73

Solve these equations.
1 $x + 9 = 20$ **2** $x + 3 = 35$ **3** $x - 7 = 11$ **4** $n - 5 = 16$ **5** $n + 2 = 14$
6 $8 + n = 9$ **7** $8 = n + 1$ **8** $13 = n - 5$ **9** $n + n = 10$

10 The diagrams show two
     equilateral triangles.
     Find x and y.

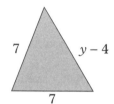

Solve these equations.
11 $3x + 7 = 13$ **12** $5x + 3 = 28$ **13** $3x - 2 = 19$ **14** $2x - 1 = 9$
15 $4x + 3 = 4$ **16** $5x + 2 = 4$ **17** $9x + 8 = 35$ **18** $3x - 42 = 12$
19 $6x - 1 = 0$ **20** $4 + 2x = 16$ **21** $0 = 3x - 66$ **22** $2x + 5 = 1$

23 Find m and n in the
     two rectangles.

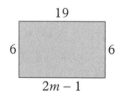
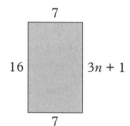

24 Find the number I am thinking of. (Start by writing an equation.)
     'If I multiply the number by 3 and then add 5, the answer
     is 26.'

Homework 2G C

2.2 pages 74–75

Solve these equations.

1 $4x + 3 = 2x - 5$ **2** $7x - 5 = 2x + 15$ **3** $8x + 2 = 3x + 17$
4 $6x + 1 = 2 - 3x$ **5** $2 - 4x = 2x - 10$ **6** $7x - 2 = 1 - 3x$
7 $7x - 4 = 4x + 8$ **8** $5 - x = 2x - 7$ **9** $x - 12 = 3x - 20$

Remove the brackets from these expressions.

10 $3(x - 1)$ **11** $2(2x + 1)$ **12** $5(1 - 2x)$ **13** $3(3x + 2)$

Solve these equations.

14 $3(x + 3) = 30$ **15** $4(x - 5) = 2$ **16** $7(2 + x) = 35$
17 $3(x + 4) = 2(x + 5)$ **18** $7(x + 2) = 4(x + 6)$ **19** $3(x - 2) = 2(x + 3)$
20 $7(x - 2) = 3x - 6$ **21** $2x + 3(x - 3) = x + 3$ **22** $3(2x - 1) - 2(x + 1) = -1$

23 Find x and y in this square.

$$2(x + 1)$$

$$4(y - 3) \qquad\qquad 8(y - 4)$$

$$3x - 1$$

Homework 2H C

2.2 pages 75–77

Reminder

$\dfrac{3}{x} = 5$

$3 = 5x$ | Multiply by x |

$\dfrac{3}{5} = x$

$\dfrac{x}{3} = -2$

$x = 3 \times -2$ | Multiply by 3 |

$x = -6$

Solve these equations.

1 $\dfrac{4}{x} = 2$ **2** $\dfrac{20}{x} = 5$ **3** $\dfrac{9}{x} = 2$ **4** $\dfrac{7}{x} = 14$ **5** $\dfrac{x}{7} = 2$ **6** $\dfrac{x}{9} = 11$

7 $\dfrac{x}{100} = -2$ **8** $\dfrac{3x}{2} = 21$ **9** $\dfrac{5}{x} = \dfrac{1}{2}$ **10** $\dfrac{3}{x} = \dfrac{1}{4}$ **11** $\dfrac{7}{x} = \dfrac{1}{4}$ **12** $\dfrac{x}{2} + 1 = 9$

13 The area of the picture is $45\,\text{cm}^2$.
Find the value of x.

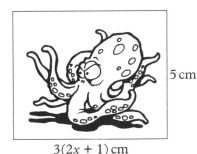

$$5\,\text{cm}$$

$$3(2x + 1)\,\text{cm}$$

In questions **14** to **18** find the number I am thinking of. (Start by writing an equation.)

14 If I multiply the number by 5 and then subtract 3, the answer is 22.

15 If I multiply the number by 6 and then add 11, the answer is 12.

16 If I treble the number and add 2, the answer is 50.

17 If I add 2 to the number and then multiply the result by 8 the answer is 40.

18 If I add 3 to the number and then multiply the result by 4, I get the same answer as when I multiply the number by 3 and subtract 2.

Homework 2I Ⓔ

2.2 pages 78–80

1 Here are some expressions involving an unknown number n.

A	B	C	D
$3n + 1$	$2(n + 2)$	$n - 7$	$2n + 1$

  a Find the value of n if the expressions A and B are equal.
  b Find the value of n if the expressions B and C are equal.
  c Which two expressions could never be equal for **any** value of n?

2 The perimeter of this rectangle is 12 cm. Find x.

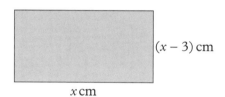
$(x - 3)$ cm
x cm

3 The length of a rectangle is 5 cm more than its width. If its perimeter is 38 cm, find its width.

4 Steve has 5 times as many marbles as Tony, but then Steve loses 3 of his. If Steve now has 22 marbles, find how many marbles Tony has.

5 Mrs Lewis has 5 times as much money with her as Mr Lewis. Mrs Lewis gives £15 to Mr Lewis so that they now both have equal amounts. How much did Mr Lewis have originally?

6 Find x in these shapes.

  a
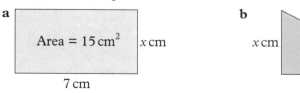
Area = 15 cm^2 x cm
7 cm

  b
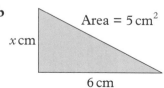
Area = 5 cm^2
x cm
6 cm

7 The angles in a triangle are $38°$, $3x°$ and $(4x - 5)°$.
Find the value of x.

8 In this rectangle, work out x
and hence find the perimeter
of the rectangle.

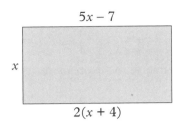

$5x - 7$

x

$2(x + 4)$

Homework 2J○

2.3 pages 80–82

1 The formula for calculating the distance travelled by a train moving at
a constant speed for a period of time is
distance = speed × time.
  a Find the distance travelled by a train travelling at 80 km/h for
  3 hours.
  b Find the distance travelled by a train which goes at 90 mph for
  5 hours.

2 The perimeter of the rectangle in the diagram
is given by
$p = 2(a + b)$
  a Find p when $a = 5$ cm and $b = 3·5$ cm.
  b Find p when $a = 6·3$ cm and $b = 3·7$ cm.

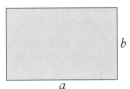

b

a

3 A formula connecting velocities with acceleration and time is
$v = u + at$
Find the value of v when $u = 25$, $a = 2$ and $t = 400$.

4 Find the value of m using the formulae and values given.
  a $m = 2ab$; $a = 5$, $b = 12$
  b $m = nt - z$; $n = 7$, $t = 4$, $z = 15$
  c $m = c^2 + d^2$; $c = 7$, $d = -2$

5 An approximate formula for the volume, V,
of a sphere is $V = 4r^3$, where r is the
radius of the sphere.
Find the value of V when $r = 3$.

6 Find the value of each expression.
  a $7x - 1$ when $x = 10$ **b** $1 - 4x$ when $x = 5$
  c $x^2 - 2$ when $x = 10$ **d** $3(1 + 4x)$ when $x = 5$.

Homework 2K ⓒ

2.3 pages 82–85

1 Find the value of each expression.

   a $4n + 11$ when $n = 15$ **b** $2(n - 7)$ when $n = 7$

   c $2n^2$ when $n = 3$ **d** $\frac{n}{4} + 8$ when $n = 36$

In questions **2** to **13** find the value of the expressions given that $a = 3$
$$b = 5$$
$$c = -1$$

2 $4a + b$ **3** ab **4** $2c$ **5** $b + c$ **6** $2(b - a)$ **7** $5(a + c)$

8 $\frac{b}{10} + a$ **9** $\frac{a + b}{4}$ **10** $a - c$ **11** abc **12** $b^2 + c$ **13** $bc + ab$

14 a Find an expression for the
     perimeter of this rectangle.
   b Find the perimeter when
     $p = 3$ and $q = 5$.

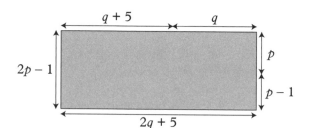

Homework 2L ⓒ

2.4 pages 86–88

Here is a sequence: 3 7 11 15	The next term in the sequence is 19. The **rule** for the sequence is 'add four'.

In questions **1** to **8** write the sequence and find the next term.

1 2, 5, 8, 11, ___   **2** 2, 7, 12, 17, ___
3 24, 22, 20, 18, ___   **4** 25, 34, 43, 52, ___
5 −3, −1, 1, 3, ___   **6** 1, 2, 4, 8, ___
7 80, 40, 20, 10, ___   **8** 1, 10, 100, 1000, ___

9 Write each sequence and find the missing number.

   a 2 8 ☐ 20   **b** 2 7 12 ☐
   c ☐ 3 6 9   **d** 1 3 9 27 ☐
   e 7 4 1 ☐   **f** 1 2 4 8 ☐

10 You are given the first term and the rule of some different sequences.
    Write the first four terms of each sequence.

	First term	**Rule**
a	7	add 11
b	84	subtract 20
c	3	double
d	200	divide by 10

11 Here is a sequence: 1, 2, 4, ___
    Explain why the next term could be either 7 or 8.

Homework 2M⒠

2.4 pages 88–90

1 The first four terms of a sequence are 3, 8, 13, 18.
The 100th term in the sequence is 498.
Work out the 101st term.

2 The first four terms of a sequence are 1, 2, 4, 8.
The 10th term in the sequence is 1024.
Work out the 9th term and the 11th term of the sequence.

3 Here is a pattern.
$$7^2 = 49$$
$$67^2 = 4489$$
$$667^2 = 444\,889$$
$$6667^2 = 44\,448\,889$$

a Use the pattern to write the value of $66\,667^2$.
b Write the square root of 44 444 448 888 889.

4 Look at the patterns of dots.

Pattern
number $n = 1$ $n = 2$ $n = 3$

a Draw the pattern for $n = 4$.
b Copy and complete the table.
c How many dots are there in pattern
   number 12?

Pattern number, n	1	2	3	4
Number of dots	6	10		

5 Copy each sequence and find the next number.
   a 1, 2, 4, 7, ___   **b** 10, 11, 9, 12, 8, ___   **c** 1, 4, 9, 16, ___   **d** 1·4, 1·6, 1·8, ___

6 Look at this number pattern.
$$1 \times 2 = 1 + 1$$
$$2 \times 3 = 2 + 4$$
$$3 \times 4 = 3 + 9$$
$$4 \times 5 = 4 + 16$$

a Write the next two lines of the pattern.
b Write the line which starts $10 \times 11 =$ ___.

Homework 2N⒠

2.4 pages 91–94

> For the sequence 3, 6, 9, 12, the nth term is $3n$.
> For the sequence 3, 5, 7, 9, the nth term is $2n + 1$.

1 Select the correct formula for the nth term of each sequence.

$\boxed{7n}$ $\boxed{10n}$

$\boxed{5n + 1}$

$\boxed{4n}$ $\boxed{5n}$

$\boxed{10n + 2}$

  a 4, 8, 12, 16, ...
  b 5, 10, 15, 20, ...
  c 10, 20, 30, 40, ...
  d 7, 14, 21, 28, ...
  e 6, 11, 16, 21, ...
  f 12, 22, 32, 42, ...

2 The first five terms of a sequence are
        4   7   10   13   16
  Copy and complete this sentence.
        'The nth term of the sequence is $3n + \square$'.

3 Find the nth term of each sequence.
  a 4, 6, 8, 10, 12, ...
  b 4, 9, 14, 19, 24, ...
  c 11, 20, 29, 38, 47, ...

4 Here are three patterns.

Pattern 1   Pattern 2   Pattern 3

  a Draw Pattern 4.
  b Copy and complete the table.

Pattern number	1	2	3	4	5
Number of dots	1	5	9		

  c How many dots do you need for Pattern 20?
  d Find an expression for the number of dots in Pattern number n.

5 The nth term of a sequence is $6n - 3$.
  Find the 5th term of the sequence.

6 The nth term of a sequence is $40 - 3n$.
  Find the 7th term of the sequence.

Homework 20 Ⓔ

2.4 pages 94–97

1 Here is a pattern of U-shapes.

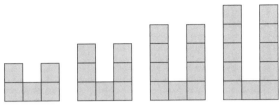

Pattern 1   Pattern 2   Pattern 3   Pattern 4

  a How many squares do you need for Pattern 6?
  b How many squares do you need for Pattern n?

2 Find the nth term of each sequence.
  a $5, 8, 11, 14, \ldots$ **b** $11, 17, 23, 29, \ldots$ **c** $1, 9, 17, 25, \ldots$

3 The diagrams show polygons with diagonals drawn from one vertex.

  $n = 4$ sides $n = 5$ sides $n = 6$ sides
  $d = 1$ diagonal $d = 2$ diagonals $d = 3$ diagonals

  Find a formula connecting d and n. Write '$d = $ _____.'

4 Look at this pattern.
  $3^2 - 2^2 = 2 \times 3 - 1$
  $4^2 - 3^2 = 2 \times 4 - 1$
  $5^2 - 4^2 = 2 \times 5 - 1$

  Use the pattern to help you copy and complete these.
  a $6^2 - 5^2 = $ _____
  b $15^2 - \square = $ _____

5 The nth term of a sequence is
     $(2n)^2 + 3$
  a Find the first term.
  b Find the fifth term.

6 Here is a sequence of squares and dots.

  a How many dots will surround the diagram with a row of 20 squares?
  b How many squares are in the diagram which has 148 dots?

3 Shape and space 1

Homework 3A ⓒ

3.1 pages 102–104

1 a Write the coordinates of the points
A, B, C, ..., H.
b Write the equation of the line through
C and H.
c Write the equation of the line through
B and D.

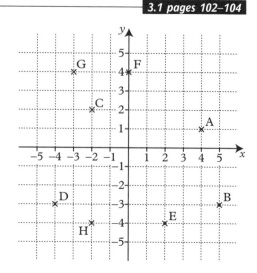

2 Draw a set of axes with values of x and y from -10 to $+10$.
Plot these points and join them up in order to make a picture.
A $(7,6)$ $(5,8)$ $(-5,8)$ $(-7,6)$ $(7,6)$ $(6,6)$ $(6,-1)$ $(8,1)$ $(10,-1)$
  $(6,-1)$ $(10,-1)$ $(10,-5)$ $(6,-5)$ $(6,-1)$ $(6,-5)$ $(-6,-5)$ $(-6,6)$
B $(-5,5)$ $(-3,5)$ $(-3,3)$ $(-5,3)$ $(-5,5)$
C $(5,5)$ $(3,5)$ $(3,3)$ $(5,3)$ $(5,5)$
D $(-5,-1)$ $(-3,-1)$ $(-3,-3)$ $(-5,-3)$ $(-5,-1)$
E $(3,-1)$ $(5,-1)$ $(5,-3)$ $(3,-3)$ $(3,-1)$
F $(-1,-1)$ $(1,-1)$ $(1,-5)$ $(-1,-5)$ $(-1,-1)$

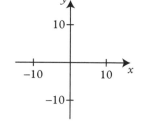

3 The graph shows four incomplete
quadrilaterals.
a Copy the diagram and complete the shapes.
b Write the coordinates of the fourth vertex
of each shape. ('vertex' means 'corner')

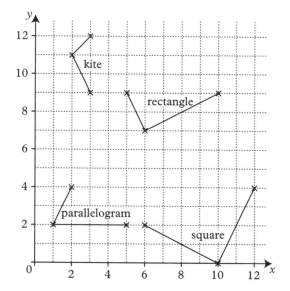

Homework 3B

3.2 pages 108–109

Reminder

$x + y = 180°$

$a + b + c = 360°$

Find the angles marked with letters.
AB and CD are straight lines.

1

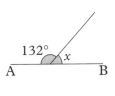

2

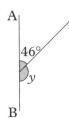

3

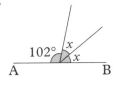

4

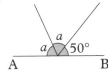

5

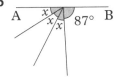

6

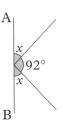

7

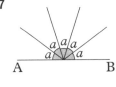

8

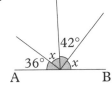

9

10

11

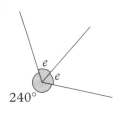

12

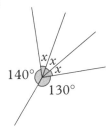

13

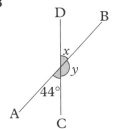

14

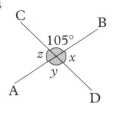

15

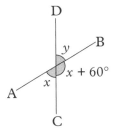

16

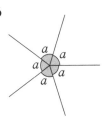

Homework 3C⊙

3.2 pages 110–112

Reminder

a 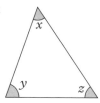 Triangle
$x + y + z = 180°$

b 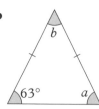 The marks show that
the triangle is isosceles.
So $a = 63°$
and $b + 63° + 63° = 180°$
$b = 54°$

Find the angles marked with letters.

1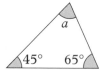

2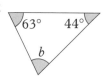

3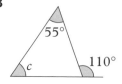

4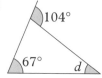

5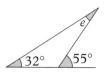

6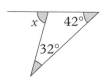

7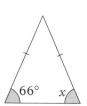

8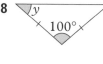

9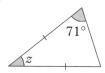

10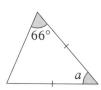

11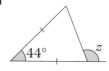

12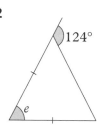

13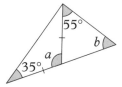

14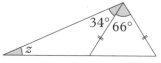

15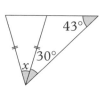

16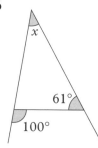

Homework 3DC

Reminder

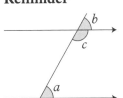

$a = b$
$a + c = 180°$

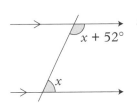

$x + (x + 52°) = 180°$
$2x + 52° = 180°$
$2x = 128°$
$x = 64°$

Find the angles marked with letters.

1

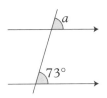

2

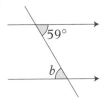

3

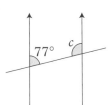

4

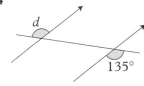

5

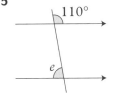

6

7

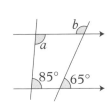

8

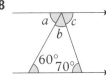

9

10

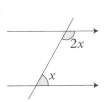

11

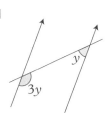

12

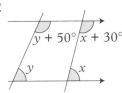

13

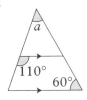

14

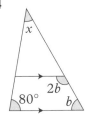

15

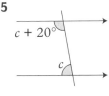

16

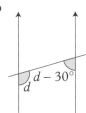

Homework 3E ⓒ

3.3 pages 116–118

Measure the angles with a protractor.

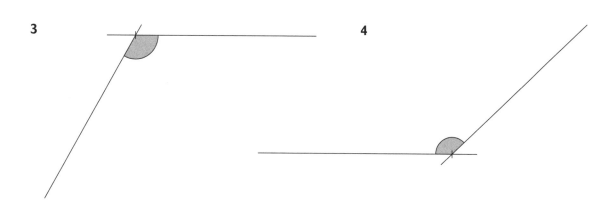

1

2

3

4

5 Draw these angles accurately.

   a 75°   **b** 145°   **c** 23°

In questions **6** to **9** measure all the angles and all the sides in each triangle.

6

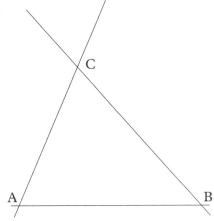

7

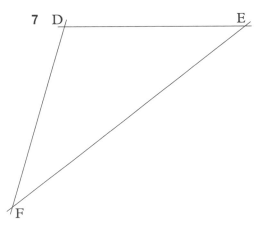

8

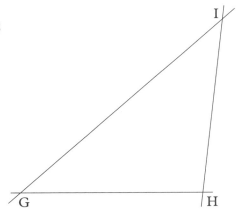

9

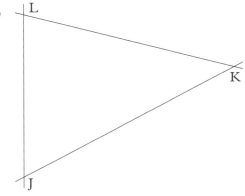

10 a Draw a line AB like the one shown.
  b Draw a line perpendicular to AB.
  c Draw a line parallel to AB.

11 Copy and complete these statements.
  Angle __ is acute.
  Angle __ is obtuse.
  Angle __ is reflex.

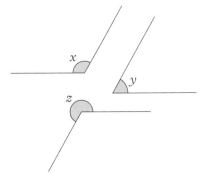

Homework 3F🇨

3.3 pages 118–120

1 Here is a sketch of a triangle, LMN.
  a Make an accurate drawing of triangle LMN.
  b Measure the size of angle M on your diagram.

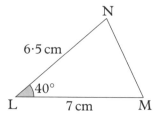

In questions **2** to **4** draw accurate full-size diagrams and measure the lengths of the sides marked with letters.

2

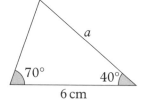

3

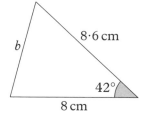

4

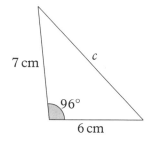

5 Susie is 80 m from the foot, A, of a vertical pylon, AB. Angle ASB = 28°.
  a Make an accurate scale drawing of the triangle using a scale of 1 cm to 10 m.
  b Find the actual height of the pylon.

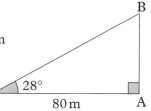

Homework 3G🇨

3.3 pages 119–120

1 Follow these steps to draw a triangle with sides 8 cm, 6 cm and 4 cm.

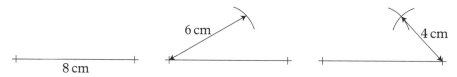

In questions **2** to **4** construct the triangles using a ruler and a pair of compasses. Measure the angles, marked with letters.

2

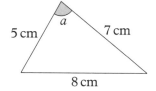

3

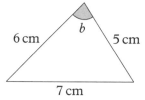

4

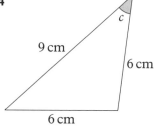

5 a Draw a line, AB, of length 8 cm.

A _____ B

b Mark the point M at the midpoint of AB.
c Draw a circle with radius 4 cm and centre M. The circle will pass through A and B.
d Mark any two points P and Q on the circle.
e Measure the angles APB and AQB. What do you notice?

Homework 3H**ᴄ**

3.3 pages 121–123

1 a Copy this net and fold it to make a cube.
b Which face is opposite face A on the cube?

```
    A
B C D E
  F
```

2 Here are four objects.

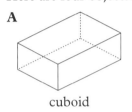
cuboid

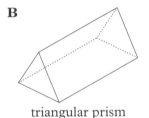
triangular prism

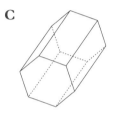
hexagonal prism

square-based pyramid

Copy and complete the table.

Shape	Number of edges	Number of faces	Numbers of vertices
A		6	
B			
C			
D			

3 Write the mathematical name of each of these 3-D shapes.

a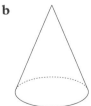

b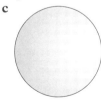

c

4 a What is the name of a triangle with two equal angles?
b What four-sided shape has all sides the same length and all angles equal?
c What is the name of an eight-sided shape?
d What name can you call any many-sided shape?

Homework 3I C

3.3–3.5 pages 123–129

Use only a pencil, a straight edge and a pair of compasses.

1 Draw a line PQ of length 7 cm.
Construct the perpendicular bisector of PQ.

2 Draw a line AB and **construct** the perpendicular to the
line segment AB that passes through the point C.

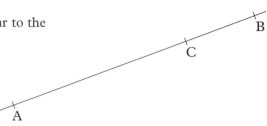

3 Draw two lines at an angle of about 45°.
Construct the bisector of the angle.

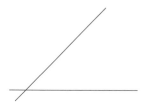

4 Make a list of the pairs of
shapes that are **congruent**.

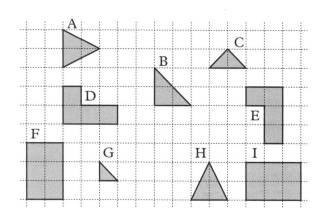

5 Which shapes in the diagram in question **4** are **similar** but **not**
congruent?

6 a Copy each of these shapes and draw all their lines of
symmetry.
b For each shape state the order of rotational symmetry.

   i   **ii**   **iii**

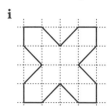 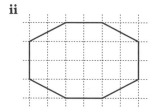 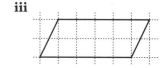

Homework 3J C

3.6 pages 131–134

1 a Write the correct name of each quadrilateral.

i 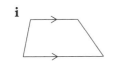 **ii** 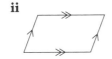 **iii**   **iv**   **v**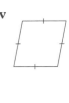

b In which of the quadrilaterals in part **a** do the diagonals always cross at right angles?

Find the angles in questions **2** to **14**.

2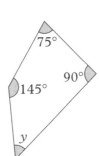

3

4

5

6

Regular hexagon –
O is the centre.

7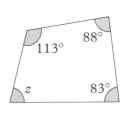

Regular octagon –
O is the centre.

8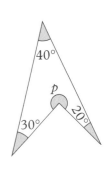

kite

9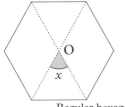

trapezium

10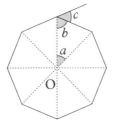

11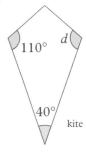

12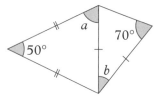

13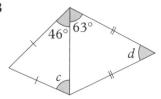

14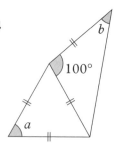

Homework 3K ⓒ

3.8 pages 137–144

1 This shape is drawn on cm squared paper.
  a Find the area of the shape.
  b Find the perimeter of the shape.

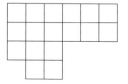

2 Calculate the area of each rectangle.

  a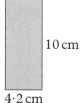
  10 cm
  4·2 cm

  b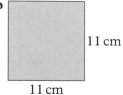
  11 cm
  11 cm

  c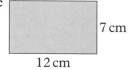
  7 cm
  12 cm

3 Find the perimeter of each of the rectangles in question **2**.

4 Find the area of each triangle. All lengths are in cm.

  a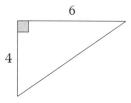
  6
  4

  b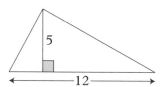
  5
  12

  c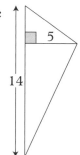
  5
  14

5 The area of this picture is 84 cm².
  Calculate the value of x.

x cm

8 cm

6 The area of this triangle is $30\,\text{cm}^2$.
Calculate its height.

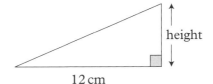

height

12 cm

Homework 3L Ⓔ

3.8 pages 139–144

1 Find the area of each shape. All lengths are in cm.

a
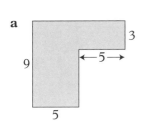

3

9 ←5→

5

b
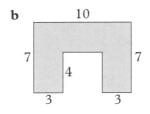

10

7 7

4

3   3

c
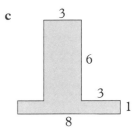

3

6

3

8   1

2 Find the perimeter of each shape in question **1**.

3 Find the area of the triangle formed by joining the points
$(1, 1)$, $(6, 1)$, $(6, 4)$.

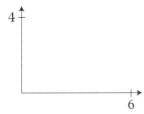

4

6

4 A picture measuring 40 cm by 30 cm has a border 10 cm wide.
What is the area of the border?

5 Diane wants to cover a wall measuring 5 m by 3 m with
square tiles measuring 50 cm by 50 cm. How many tiles will
she need?

6 A rectangle has a perimeter of 28 m and a length of 7·5 m.
What is its area?

7 A field measures 250 m by 100 m.
a What is the area of the field in m^2?
b What is the area of the field in hectares?
(1 hectare $= 10\,000\,\text{m}^2$)

8 (More difficult) Find the area of the triangle formed by joining the
points $(1, 2)$, $(3, 6)$ and $(6, 3)$.

4 Handling data 1

Homework 4A 🅒

4.1 pages 152–163

1 The graph shows a return journey
by car from London.
  a How far is the car from London
  at its first stop?
  b When does the car arrive
  back in London?
  c What is the speed of the car
    i from 9:00 to 10:00
    ii from 10:15 to 10:45
    iii from 11:00 to 12:00?

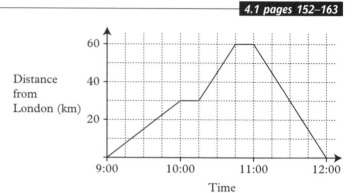

2 The graph shows Eric's return
journey from York.
  a How far from York is Eric at
  12:45?
  b At what time is Eric 20 km from
  York for the second time?
  c Find Eric's speed in the sections
  marked A, B, C, D and E.

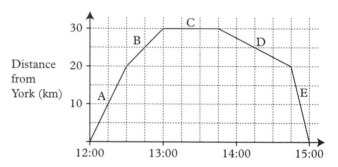

3 This graph converts Australian dollars to pounds.
  a Convert into pounds
    i 140 dollars **ii** 84 dollars **iii** 100 dollars.
  b Convert into dollars
    i £20 **ii** £50 **iii** £60.

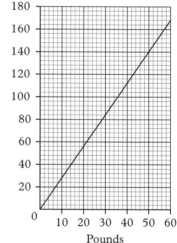

4 Draw a graph which shows that the
temperature in an oven stays the same
for a time and then rises quickly.

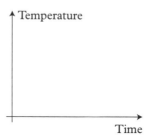

5 The travel graph shows Sue's journey to see her parents.
Give a brief description of her journey.
Give as much detail as possible.

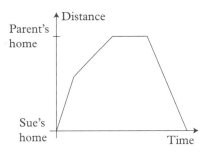

Homework 4B❻

4.2 pages 167–174

In questions **1** to **5** find
a the mean   **b** the median   **c** the mode.
(Begin each question by writing the numbers in order of size.)

1 3, 4, 6, 9, 3, 2, 8

2 3, 1, 7, 4, 1, 7, 4, 1, 8

3 5, 5, 6, 3, 7, 7, 3, 5, 6, 9, 10

4 11, 4, 12, 8, 12, 5, 11, 12, 9, 12

5 6, 2, 7, 1, 7, 10, 4, 7, 1, 6

6 a Calculate the mean of these numbers.
    3, 7, 6, 5, 4, 3, 8, 14
b Calculate the new mean when the 8 is removed.

7 Max counted the number of letters in the words on one page of
a book and got these results.

4	2	4	3	5	3	4	2	5	3
5	6	2	4	7	1	7	1	8	2
1	8	6	3	4	9	3	8	3	7
4	2	3	5	4	2	6	5	1	4
3	6	3	1	6	4	3	4	7	5

Number of letters	Tally	Frequency
1	LHT	5
2		
3		
⋮		

a Make a tally chart like the one shown.
b What number of letters in a word was the mode?

8 Find the range for each set of numbers.
a 3, 4, 5, 3, 4, 4, 3, 5, 5, 4
b 0, 3, 6, −3, 2, 7, 4, −2, 8, −2
c 1, 3, 4, 2, 3, 4, 7, 15, 5, 0, 11, 2

9 The weights of 5 cats are 3·2 kg, 2·7 kg, 4·1 kg, 3 kg, 4·5 kg and the
weights of 5 dogs are 4·7 kg, 5·4 kg, 5·2 kg, 4·1 kg, 6 kg.
a Find the mean weight of the cats.
b Find the mean weight of the dogs.
c Find the mean weight of all the animals.

Homework 4C●

4.2 pages 167–180

1 a Write five numbers so that their median is 9.
   b Write six numbers so that their range is 10.
   c Write ten numbers so that their mode is 4.

2 The table gives information about the
   number of goals scored by the players
   in a team.
   a How many players were there?
   b Copy the table and use it to work out the
      mean number of goals scored.

Goals scored	Number of players	
1	7	
2	6	
3	4	
4	3	

3 Here are five numbers in order of size: $3, 4, 7, 11, n$.
   a The range of the numbers is 17. Find n.
   b Find the mean of the numbers.

4 Joshua tested a boxful of batteries to see how long they lasted.
   The results are in the table.
   a How many batteries did Joshua test?
   b Calculate an estimate of the mean time that a
      battery lasted.
   c Explain why your answer is an **estimate**.

Time (t hours)	Frequency
$0 \le t < 4$	6
$4 \le t < 8$	8
$8 \le t < 12$	15
$12 \le t < 16$	11
$16 \le t < 20$	10

Homework 4D●

4.3 pages 181–185

1 The pie chart shows the destinations of 240 people.
   a Simplify these fractions (that is 'cancel down').

   i $\frac{90}{360}$ **ii** $\frac{60}{360}$ **iii** $\frac{150}{360}$

   b What fraction of the people went to
      i France   **ii** Italy   **iii** Spain?

   c How many people went to
      i France   **ii** Spain   **iii** Portugal?

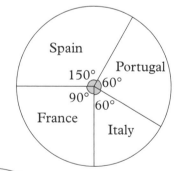

2 Jan asked 240 people about their favourite pets.
   a What percentage of people chose
      i dogs   **ii** birds?
   b How many people chose
      i dogs   **ii** birds?

3 Malcolm asked 90 girls to name their favourite sport.
Here are the results.

Sport	Netball	Hockey	Football	Swimming	Tennis
Number of girls	15	33	25	11	6

a Draw a pie chart to show this information.
b Mellisa did a similar survey of 90 girls at her school. In a pie chart
of her results the angle for football was 64°. How many girls in
Mellisa's school chose football?

Homework 4E C

4.4 pages 187–189

1 Here are the marks in a maths test.
54   61   82   48   67   84   80   71   60   89
47   85   71   57   68   81   55   69   70   65

Copy and complete the table.

Mark	Tally	Frequency
41–50		
51–60		
61–70		
71–80		
81–90		

2 The bar chart shows age groups on three different holidays.

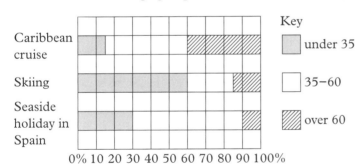

a What percentage of holidaymakers were
  i between 35 and 60 on the seaside
     holiday in Spain
  ii under 35 on the skiing holiday
  iii over 60 on the Caribbean cruise?
b Describe the main difference between the top two bars.
  Why do you think they are so different?

3 The table shows the petrol consumption of a car in litres per 100 km at different road speeds.

Road speed (km/h)	20	30	40	50	60	70	80	90	100
Consumption (litres per 100 km)	5·5	4·8	4·4	4	4	4·3	4·9	5·8	7·2

a Draw a pair of axes with road speed on the horizontal axis and petrol consumption on the vertical axis.
b Plot the nine points from the table and join them with a smooth curve.
c From your graph estimate the most economical road speed for the car.
d Estimate the consumption in litres per 100 km at a speed of 95 km/h.
e If petrol costs 106p per litre, find the cost of a journey of 200 km if the car travels at a steady speed of 90 km/h.

Homework 4F C

4.5 pages 194–196

1 The stem-and-leaf diagram shows the scores of a basketball team in one season.
a How many games did the team play?
b What was the team's lowest score?
c What was the team's median score?
d One of the scores is chosen at random. Find the probability that the score is over 60.

```
3 | 7  9
4 | 0  4  8
5 | 1  5  5  6  8  8
6 | 3  4  7  7  8
7 | 3  7
```

Key: 6|3 means 63

2 The stem-and-leaf diagram shows the heights of the players in a basketball team.
a What was the height of the tallest player?
b What was the median height of the players?
c What was the range of the heights?

```
16 | 9
17 | 5  8
18 | 0  3  5  7
19 | 1  4  4
20 | 4
```

Key 18|0 means 180 cm

3 Here are the marks of 21 students in a test.

25   42   51   56   63   48   35
30   64   48   27   71   58   34
44   59   72   36   51   68   47

a Draw a stem-and-leaf diagram to show the marks.
b Write the range of the marks.
c Find the median marks.

stem	leaf
2	
3	
4	
5	
6	
7	

5   Number 2

Homework 5A C

5.1 pages 201–203

Work out.

1 32×41 **2** 45×37 **3** 214×35

4 Sandra earns £315 per week. How much does she earn in a year?

5 Work out.

   a $504 \div 14$ **b** $828 \div 23$ **c** $2790 \div 45$

6 There are 18 cans of tuna in a box. How many boxes are needed for 990 cans?

7 A cinema has 33 rows of seats, with 15 seats in each row. The price of a ticket is £12.

   a How many seats are there in the cinema?

   b Calculate the income from the sale of tickets for 10 performances if all the seats are sold.

Homework 5B C

5.2 pages 203–206

1 What fraction of this shape is shaded?
Give your answer in its simplest form.

2 Draw this diagram and shade in $\frac{2}{3}$ of the rectangle.

3 What fraction does each of these number lines show?

4 Cancel down these fractions.

   a $\frac{8}{12}$ **b** $\frac{9}{15}$ **c** $\frac{14}{21}$ **d** $\frac{4}{16}$ **e** $\frac{15}{25}$

5 Copy and complete by filling in the missing number.

   a $\frac{1}{3} = \frac{\square}{6}$ **b** $\frac{2}{5} = \frac{\square}{10}$ **c** $\frac{3}{4} = \frac{\square}{12}$

   d $1 = \frac{\square}{7}$ **e** $\frac{1}{6} = \frac{\square}{18}$ **f** $\frac{7}{8} = \frac{\square}{24}$

6 Write the fractions $\frac{9}{19}, \frac{2}{5}, \frac{1}{2}$ in order of size, smallest first.

7 Here are some number cards.

a Use two cards to make a fraction that is equal to $\frac{3}{9}$.

b Use two cards to make the largest possible fraction that is less than one.

c Use three cards to make a fraction that is equal to $\frac{1}{4}$.

Homework 5C⊙

5.2 pages 208–211

Work out these amounts.

1 $\frac{1}{3}$ of 36   **2** $\frac{1}{5}$ of 30   **3** $\frac{2}{3}$ of 24   **4** $\frac{3}{5}$ of 40   **5** $\frac{5}{6}$ of 18   **6** $\frac{2}{9}$ of 45

7 There are 36 biscuits in a packet.
Shirin eats $\frac{1}{4}$ of the biscuits and Anjie eats $\frac{2}{3}$ of the biscuits.
How many biscuits are left in the packet?

8 Louise wins a prize of £240 and decides to save $\frac{3}{5}$ of it. How much does she save?

9 Which of these fractions are equal to $\frac{3}{4}$?

$\frac{8}{12}$ $\frac{15}{20}$ $\frac{7}{10}$ $\frac{9}{12}$

10 The diagram shows a piece of wood with a mark for a screw hole near each end. Draw an accurate full-size diagram of the piece of wood. Show on the diagram where you would make two more holes so that all four holes are equally spaced in a straight line along the wood.

11 The scales show that 12 cubes balance with 8 discs.
Two discs are now removed.
How many cubes must be removed so that the scales will still balance?

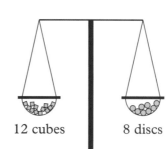

12 cubes   8 discs

Homework 5D ⓒ

5.2 pages 211–215

1 Work out.

a $\frac{1}{8} + \frac{4}{8}$ **b** $\frac{1}{5} + \frac{2}{5}$ **c** $\frac{3}{11} + \frac{4}{11}$ **d** $\frac{5}{9} - \frac{1}{9}$

2 Copy and complete.

a $\frac{1}{2} + \frac{1}{3} = \frac{3}{6} + \frac{\square}{6} =$ **b** $\frac{1}{4} + \frac{1}{5} = \frac{5}{20} + \frac{\square}{20} =$ **c** $\frac{1}{4} + \frac{1}{6} =$

d $\frac{3}{4} - \frac{1}{8} =$ **e** $\frac{1}{3} - \frac{1}{4} =$ **f** $\frac{2}{5} - \frac{3}{8} =$

3 Change into improper fractions

a $1\frac{1}{4}$ **b** $2\frac{2}{3}$ **c** $3\frac{1}{2}$ **d** $5\frac{2}{5}$ **e** $3\frac{1}{7}$

> For example,
> $2\frac{3}{4} = \frac{11}{4}$.

4 Work out.

a $1\frac{1}{4} + 1\frac{1}{3}$ **b** $2\frac{2}{3} + 1\frac{1}{4}$ **c** $3\frac{1}{2} + 5\frac{2}{5}$

5 Work out.

a $\frac{3}{4} \times \frac{1}{5}$ **b** $\frac{3}{8} \times \frac{4}{5}$ **c** $\frac{5}{9} \times \frac{1}{2}$ **d** $\frac{11}{4} \times \frac{3}{10}$

6 Copy and complete.

$\frac{2}{3} \div \frac{3}{5} = \frac{2}{3} \times \frac{5}{3} =$

7 Work out.

a $\frac{2}{5} \div \frac{1}{2}$ **b** $\frac{3}{4} \div \frac{1}{3}$ **c** $\frac{1}{6} \div \frac{4}{5}$ **d** $\frac{4}{5} \div \frac{1}{4}$

Homework 5E ⓒ

5.2 pages 214–215

1 Change into mixed fractions.

a $\frac{8}{3}$ **b** $\frac{9}{4}$ **c** $\frac{11}{5}$ **d** $\frac{12}{5}$ **e** $\frac{7}{2}$

> For example,
> $\frac{7}{3} = 2\frac{1}{3}$.

2 Work out.

a $2\frac{1}{2} \times \frac{4}{5}$ **b** $3\frac{3}{4} \times \frac{2}{3}$ **c** $3\frac{3}{4} \div \frac{2}{3}$ **d** $3\frac{3}{4} - \frac{2}{3}$

3 Jack has £810. He spends $\frac{2}{5}$ on a holiday and gives $\frac{1}{3}$ to his daughter.

How much of the original £810 is left?

4 a A coach party stopped at a motorway service station. $\frac{1}{4}$ of the party
had a hot meal and $\frac{3}{5}$ bought a sandwich. The rest of them were too
unwell to eat anything.

What fraction of the group bought something to eat?

b $\frac{2}{3}$ of those who bought a sandwich also bought a drink. What fraction
of the whole group bought a sandwich and a drink?

5 In a shoal of baby dolphins, 40% can swim
unaided and $\frac{3}{8}$ can only swim with a ring.

Which of the two groups is bigger?

6 Fill in the missing numbers so
that the answer is always $\frac{1}{4}$.

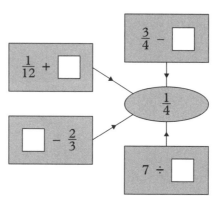

Homework 5F **C**

5.3 pages 215–220

1 For each diagram write   **a** the fraction that is shaded
                                b the percentage that is shaded.

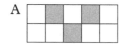   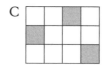

2 Change to percentages.

a $\frac{3}{5}$ **b** $\frac{1}{20}$ **c** $\frac{3}{10}$ **d** $\frac{11}{25}$ **e** $\frac{45}{60}$

> **Reminder:** To
> change a fraction
> to a percentage,
> you multiply by
> 100%.

3 In a test Nicki got 14 out of 20. What is her percentage mark?

4 In a survey 37 out of 40 pandas said that they
preferred organic bamboo to bamboo grown
with artificial fertilisers. What percentage was that?

5 In a 60-minute maths lesson, Wayne spent 18 minutes 'trying to
find his calculator'. For what percentage of the lesson was he
searching?

6 Work out these amounts.
   a 20% of £55   **b** 5% of £400   **c** 7% of £600

7 There are 240 people working in a factory and 65% get to work by car.
How many people get to work by car?

Homework 5G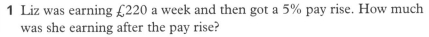

5.3 pages 220–222

1 Liz was earning £220 a week and then got a 5% pay rise. How much
was she earning after the pay rise?

2 Work out the new prices.
   a Increase a price of £80 by 4%.
   b Increase a price of £240 by 11%.
   c Reduce a price of £700 by 8%.

3 **a** Which is greater, 60% or $\frac{2}{3}$?

   b Which is greater, $\frac{3}{4}$ or 70%?

4 Abraham bought a watch for £55 and then sold it so that he made
a 20% profit. At what price did he sell the watch?

5 Find the total bill.
   3 brushes at £2·40 each
   4 tins of paint at £3·60 each
   VAT at 17·5% is added to the total.

6 Jackie has seen two microwaves for sale.
   Find the difference in the prices of the microwaves.

A	B
£ 135 including VAT	£ 120 plus VAT

7 Harry invested £1400 in a bank at 4·5% interest.
How much did Harry have in the bank after one year?

Homework 5H

5.3 pages 220–222

> After an increase of 8%, the price of a boat is £7560.
> What was the price before the increase?
> $$108\% \text{ of old price} = £7560$$
> $$1\% \text{ of old price} = £(7560 \div 108)$$
> $$100\% \text{ of old price} = \frac{7560}{108} \times 100 = £7000$$

1 After an increase of 5%, the price of a printer is £472·50.
  What was the price before the increase?

2 After a 7% pay rise, the salary of Mrs Everett was £24 075.
  What was her salary before the pay rise?

3 After a decrease of 10% the price of a telephone is £58·50.
  Copy and complete.
  $$90\% \text{ of old price} = £58·50$$
  $$1\% \text{ of old price} = £\square$$
  $$100\% \text{ of old price} = £\square$$

4 During one year the value of Mr Pert's house went down by 6%.
  Its value was then £60 160. What was its value before the decrease?

5 Copy the table and fill in the missing prices.

	Item	Old price	New price	Percentage change
a	i-pod		£180·50	5% decrease
b	Computer		£391·60	11% decrease
c	House		£103 090	22% increase

Homework 5I

5.3 pages 225–227

> $$\text{Percentage increase} = \frac{\text{actual increase}}{\text{original value}} \times \frac{100}{1}$$

1 The price of a motor bike was increased from £2400 to £2496.
  Calculate the percentage increase in the price.

2 Calculate the percentage increase.

	Original price	Final price
a	£850	£901
b	£14 600	£14 892
c	£66·50	£73·15

3 The population of a village went down from 880 to 836. Calculate
  the percentage decrease in the population.

4 After the success of the film 'Man-Tiger' the actor's fee went up from £2 million to £3·25 million. What was the percentage increase in his fee?

5 Steve bought a car at an auction for £1600 and two weeks later sold it for £1824. Calculate Steve's percentage profit.

6 Max needed to cut down some trees on his land. He hired a chain saw and the cost of hiring was

> £25 for the first day
> £17·50 for each extra day

The total cost of hiring the chain saw was £112·50.
For how many days altogether did Max hire the chain saw?

Homework 5J ⓒ

5.3 pages 227–228

> £8000 is invested at 3% compound interest.
> After 1 year, investment = 8000 × 1·03 = £8240
> After 2 years, investment = 8000 × 1·03 × 1·03 = £8487·20
> After n years, investment = $8000 \times 1·03^n$

1 A bank pays 5% compound interest per annum. Mrs Cameron puts £5000 in the bank. How much has she after
  a one year   **b** two years?

2 Nadia invested £3000 for 3 years at 4% per annum compound interest. How much money did she have at the end of three years?

3 Tom put £3000 in a savings account offering 6% per year compound interest. How much did he have in the account after 3 years?

4 Sasha saved £4000 at 4% simple interest per year.
Sylvie saved £4000 at 3·5% compound interest per year.
Calculate how much each person had in their savings after 5 years.

5 A tennis club has 250 members.
The number of members increases by 20% each year.
Calculate the number of members after 3 years.

Homework 5K

5.4 pages 228–232

> Share £64 in the ratio 3 : 5
> Total number of shares = 3 + 5 = 8
> So one share = £64 ÷ 8 = £8
> So three shares = £24 and five shares = £40.
> The two amounts are £24 and £40.

1 In a hotel there are 54 chairs and 9 tables.
  Find the ratio of chairs to tables.

2 In a class at school there are 12 boys and 15 girls.
  Write the ratio boys : girls, giving your answer in its
  simplest form.

3 Write these ratios in a simpler form.
  a 12 : 8   **b** 20 : 50   **c** 18 : 24   **d** 25 : 40

4 In a class there are 18 boys and 7 girls. What fraction of the class
  are girls?

5 Express each ratio in its simplest form. Remember to use the same
  units in both parts of the ratio.
  a £5 : 80p   **b** 25p : £2   **c** 600 g to 1 kg

6 Divide £75 between two people in the ratio 2 : 3

7 Share £800 between two people in the ratio 1 : 4

8 A sum of £1000 is divided in the ratio 1 : 3 : 4 What is the smallest
  share?

9 Alf, Betty and Charles share a cake weighing 450 g in the ratio 4 : 5 : 6
  How heavy was Charles's share?

10 Pat and Ray share the cost of a coach trip in the ratio 3 : 1.
  What percentage of the cost does Ray pay?

Homework 5L

5.4 pages 233–235

1 Two squares are shown with their perimeters
  a Write the ratio of the lengths of their sides.
  b Find the ratio of their areas.

perimeter
= 16 cm

perimeter
= 24 cm

2 On a map with scale 1 : 10 000, the distance between two points is 4 cm.
  Find the actual distance between the two points, giving your answer
  in metres.

3 The scale of a map is 1: 25 000. What is the actual distance in metres between two points which are 2 cm apart on the map?

4 Copy and complete the table.

	Map scale	Length on map	Actual length on land
a	1 : 50 000	10 cm	☐ km
b	1 : 80 000	8 cm	☐ km
c	1 : 4500	5 cm	☐ m

5 The distance between two points is 600 m. How far apart will they be, in cm, on a map of scale 1 : 1000?

6 The scale of a map is 1 : 50 000. The actual distance between two towns is 2 km. How far apart, in cm, will they be on the map?

7 The total weight of 8 cakes is 816 g. How much do 5 cakes weigh?

8 How much would 3 CDs cost, if 10 CDs cost £85?

9 Eight trees cost £200.
  a What is the cost of 11 trees?
  b How many trees can be bought for £825?

Homework 5M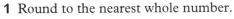

5.7 pages 245–249

> 47·6̲2 = 48 to the nearest whole number.
> 218·4̲ = 218 to three significant figures.
> 628̲0 = 6300 to two significant figures.
> 12·6̲72 = 12·7 to one decimal place.

Look at the digit underlined to see if it is '5 or more'.

1 Round to the nearest whole number.
  a 18·72   **b** 242·1   **c** 11·54   **d** 3014·33
  e 7·95   **f** 25·55   **g** 734·203   **h** 0·97

2 Round to two significant figures.
  a 46·7   **b** 259·2   **c** 40·23   **d** 378·8   **e** 7832   **f** 85 999

3 Round to one significant figure.
  a 807   **b** 83   **c** 45 617   **d** 1·95   **e** 0·078   **f** 0·0342

4 Write these numbers correct to one decimal place.
  a 11·34   **b** 8·761   **c** 211·72   **d** 0·871   **e** 0·324   **f** 16·02

5 Write these numbers correct to two decimal places.
  a 1·672   **b** 8·758   **c** 0·446   **d** 0·071   **e** 85·222   **f** 16·955

Use a calculator to work these out, giving your answers to
the accuracy required.

6 $5 \cdot 2 \div 0 \cdot 142$ (1 dp)   **7** $8 \cdot 14 \times 0 \cdot 72$ (2 dp)   **8** $6 \cdot 23^2$ (1 dp)

9 $11 \cdot 74 \times 6 \cdot 05$ (1 dp)   **10** $\sqrt{92 \cdot 4}$ (1 dp)   **11** $18 \cdot 7 \div 19$ (1 dp)

12 $85 \cdot 2 \div 7 \cdot 1$ (2 sf)   **13** $215 \div 82$ (2 sf)   **14** $98 \cdot 4^2$ (3 sf)

15 $18 \cdot 2 \times 3 \cdot 67$ (nearest whole number)   **16** $6 \cdot 2^3$ (nearest whole number)

Homework 5N🅒

5.8 pages 249–251

> To estimate the answer to a calculation, round the numbers in
> the calculation, for example, $19 \cdot 2 \times 4 \cdot 82 \approx 20 \times 5 \quad \approx 100$
> $$724 \div 52 \cdot 7 \approx 700 \div 50 \approx 14$$

Write each calculation and decide, by estimating, which answer
is closest to the exact answer.

	Calculation	A	B	C
1	$2 \cdot 05 \times 9 \cdot 7$	10	30	20
2	$3 \cdot 8 \times 52 \cdot 3$	20	200	90
3	$96 \cdot 8 \times 3 \cdot 18$	35	150	300
4	$1 \cdot 03 \times 77 \cdot 5$	80	40	400
5	$46 \cdot 7 \times 98 \cdot 5$	500	2000	5000
6	$7 \cdot 94 \div 3 \cdot 91$	5	8	2
7	$69 \cdot 4 \div 8 \cdot 97$	7	3	70
8	$401 \cdot 4 \div 4 \cdot 19$	50	100	400
9	$10 \cdot 013 \div 97 \cdot 4$	0·2	1	0·1
10	$997 \div 2 \cdot 13$	500	800	2000

In questions **11** to **13** there are six calculations and six answers.
Write each calculation and decide, by estimating, which is the correct
answer to that calculation.

11   **a** $4 \cdot 9 \times 10 \cdot 2 =$ **b** $10 \cdot 7 \times 6 \cdot 1 =$ **c** $4 \cdot 8 \times 5 \cdot 3 =$
    d $7 \cdot 9 \times 10 \cdot 3 =$ **e** $1 \cdot 1 \times 2 \cdot 7 =$ **f** $1 \cdot 8 \times 6 \cdot 4 =$
    The answers are $25 \cdot 44, 2 \cdot 97, 81 \cdot 37, 49 \cdot 98, 65 \cdot 27, 11 \cdot 52$.

12   **a** $8 \cdot 7 \times 9 \cdot 4 =$ **b** $0 \cdot 5 \times 8 \cdot 3 =$ **c** $7 \cdot 2 \times 1 \cdot 9 =$
    d $11 \cdot 8 \times 3 \cdot 3 =$ **e** $5 \cdot 2 \times 10 \cdot 8 =$ **f** $4 \cdot 3 \times 6 \cdot 8 =$
    The answers are $29 \cdot 24, 38 \cdot 94, 81 \cdot 78, 13 \cdot 68, 56 \cdot 16, 4 \cdot 15$.

13   **a** $1 \cdot 8 \times 10 \cdot 4 =$ **b** $9 \cdot 8 \times 9 \cdot 1 =$ **c** $7 \cdot 9 \times 8 \cdot 1 =$
    d $4 \cdot 02 \times 1 \cdot 9 =$ **e** $3 \cdot 8 \times 8 \cdot 2 =$ **f** $8 \cdot 15 \times 5 \cdot 92 =$
    The answers are $63 \cdot 99, 18 \cdot 72, 31 \cdot 16, 7 \cdot 638, 48 \cdot 248, 89 \cdot 18$.

6 Algebra 2

Homework 6Aⓒ

6.1 pages 266–270

1 Here are three rectangles in which the base is twice the height. The area of each rectangle is written inside it. Use trial and improvement to find the height of each rectangle.

a
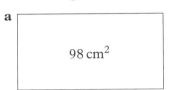
$98\,cm^2$

b

$392\,cm^2$

c
$9{\cdot}68\,m^2$

2 Find $\sqrt{91{\cdot}5}$ by trial and improvement.
You need to solve the equation $x^2 = 91{\cdot}5$.
Give your answer correct to 1 dp.
Copy and complete these steps.

Try $x = 9$ $9 \times 9 =$ _____ $x = 9$ is too small
Try $x = 10$ $10 \times 10 =$ _____ $x = 10$ is too big
Try $x = 9{\cdot}5$ _____ $\times$ _____ $=$ _____ $x = 9{\cdot}5$ is too _____
Try $x = 9{\cdot}4$ _____ $\times$ _____ $=$ _____ $x = 9{\cdot}4$ is too _____
Solution $x =$ _____ to 1 dp

3 Use the method in question **2** to find
a the cube root of 50, correct to 1 dp.
b the cube root of 210, correct to 1 dp.

4 This rectangle has width h cm.
The length is 2 cm more than the width.
The area of the rectangle is $404\,cm^2$.
Find the value of h correct to one decimal place.

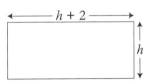

You need to solve the equation $h(h + 2) = 404$.
Copy and complete these steps.

Try $h = 17$ $17 \times 19 = 323$ $h =$ __ is too small
Try $h = 23$ $23 \times 25 = 575$ $h =$ __ is too big
Try ......

Homework 6B⊙

6.2 pages 270–271

> **Reminder**
> $3(2x + 1) = 6x + 3;$ $4(3x - 2) = 12x - 8$
> $(x + 3)(x + 7) = x(x + 7) + 3(x + 7)$
> $\qquad\qquad\quad = x^2 + 7x + 3x + 21$
> $\qquad\qquad\quad = x^2 + 10x + 21$

1 Remove the brackets.

  a $3(x + 2)$ **b** $4(x - 3)$ **c** $5(2x + 1)$ **d** $7(3x - 1)$ **e** $x(x + 1)$

  f $x(x + 4)$ **g** $x(2x + 1)$ **h** $x(x - 2)$ **i** $x(3x + 10)$

2 Remove the brackets and simplify.

  a $3(x + 2) + 2(5x + 1)$ **b** $5(x - 2) + 2(x + 1)$ **c** $2(2x - 1) + 3(x + 3)$

  d $7(2x + 1) - 3(x - 1)$ **e** $x(x + 1) + x(x + 2)$ **f** $x(x + 3) + 2x(x + 1)$

3 Copy and complete.

$$(x + 2)(x + 5) = x(x + 5) + 2(x + 5)$$
$$= x^2 + \square + 2x + \square$$
$$= \square + \square + \square$$

4 Remove the brackets and simplify.

  a $(x + 4)(x + 1)$ **b** $(x + 1)(x + 7)$ **c** $(x + 3)(x + 3)$

  d $(x + 3)(x - 2)$ **e** $(x + 4)(x - 5)$ **f** $(2x + 1)(x + 3)$

  g $(x + 4)^2$ **h** $(x + 1)^2$ **i** $(x + 4)(x - 4)$

Homework 6C⊙

6.2 pages 272–273

> **Factorise**
> $10a + 15b = 5\,(2a + 3b)$
> $3x^2 + 2x = x(3x + 2)$
> $4n^2 + 8mn + 2n = 2n(2n + 4m + 1)$

In questions **1** to **6** copy and complete the statements.

  1 $8a + 4b = 4(2a + \square)$ **2** $5a + 15b = 5(\square + 3b)$ **3** $15a + 20b = 5(\square + \square)$

  4 $7a + 21b = \square(a + 3b)$ **5** $27a - 36b = 9(\square - \square)$ **6** $4a + 8b + 4c = 4(\square + \square + \square)$

Factorise these expressions.

  7 $20x + 12y$ **8** $30x - 12y$ **9** $27x + 9y$ **10** $35x - 14y$

11 $40x + 20y$ **12** $10x + 5y + 10z$ **13** $3x^2 + 2x$ **14** $4x^2 + 2x$

15 $5x^2 + x$ **16** $x^2 - 2x$ **17** $2y^2 + 5y$ **18** $12x^2 + 21x$

Solve these equations.
19 $3(x + 3) = 30$ **20** $4(x - 5) = 2$ **21** $6(1 + x) = 9$ **22** $10(x - 3) = 5$
23 $5(x + 1) = 7$ **24** $3(x + 4) = 2(x + 5)$

25 The area of this rectangle is 63 cm^2.
Form an equation and then solve it to
find the value of x.

7 cm

$(2x - 1) \text{ cm}$

Homework 6D 🜚

6.3 pages 273–274

> Make x the subject of each formula.
> **a** $x + t = m$ so $x = m - t$
> **b** $ax = h$ so $x = \dfrac{h}{a}$
> **c** $hx + c = u^2$ so $hx = u^2 - c$ so $x = \dfrac{u^2 - c}{h}$

Make x the subject.
1 $x + t = h$ **2** $x - v = w$ **3** $x + 2a = c$ **4** $x - m = 2n$
5 $2x + t = s$ **6** $3x - v = w$ **7** $2x + n = 2n$ **8** $ax = b$
9 $nx = c$ **10** $cx + d = h$ **11** $nx - h = t$ **12** $ax - b = c + d$

Now make x the subject of these formulae.
13 $hx - h = a$ **14** $px + p = q$ **15** $nx - h = h$ **16** $a(x - b) = c$
17 $c(x - d) = e$ **18** $m(x + m) = n^2$ **19** $k(x - a) = t$ **20** $h(x - h) = k$
21 $m(x + b) = n$ **22** $Ha + x = m$ **23** $at + x = u$ **24** $v + x = 2v + w$

25 Copy and complete.

a $\dfrac{x}{t} = a$ **b** $\dfrac{x}{m} = u^2$ **c** $\dfrac{a}{x} = t$
$x = \boxed{} \times a$ $x = \boxed{}$ $a = tx$
$\dfrac{a}{\boxed{}} = x$

Make x the subject.
26 $\dfrac{x}{m} = t$ **27** $\dfrac{x}{c} = c$ **28** $\dfrac{x}{m} = a + b$ **29** $\dfrac{a}{x} = c$ **30** $\dfrac{t}{x} = u$ **31** $\dfrac{m}{x} = n$

Homework 6E ⓒ

6.3 pages 274–275

In each equation, make x the subject.

1 $tx = a$
2 $\dfrac{x}{c} = h$
3 $bx + u = u$
4 $a(x + t) = y$

5 $\dfrac{c}{x} = a$
6 $\dfrac{tx}{d} = w$
7 $dx + n = h$
8 $h = Ax$

9 $n = \dfrac{x}{m}$
10 $\dfrac{ax}{k} = b$
11 $k = cx - m$
12 $D(x + d) = m$

13 $\dfrac{h}{x} = a$
14 $hx = t$
15 $z = bx - a$
16 $d = \dfrac{b}{x}$

17 $kx + p = q$
18 $\dfrac{dx}{a} = u$
19 $d = Ax + L$
20 $dx = k$

21 $k = b(x - A)$
22 $k = \dfrac{D}{x}$
23 $r = \dfrac{Bx}{y}$
24 $\dfrac{x}{t} = n$

25 Copy and complete.

a $ax^2 = m$
$\quad x^2 = \dfrac{m}{\square}$
$\quad x = \pm\sqrt{\dfrac{m}{\square}}$

b $v - x = q$
$\quad v = q + x$
$\quad \square - \square = x$

c $v^2 = n - x$
$\quad v^2 + x = n$
$\quad x = n - \square$

Make x the subject.

26 $mx^2 = a$
27 $hx^2 = t$
28 $x^2 + a = b$
29 $x^2 - t = m$
30 $h - x = a$

31 $b - x = q$
32 $b - x = u$
33 $v_2 - ax = c$
34 $c = d - mx$
35 $h = a - nx$

36 $a^2 = a - x$
37 $b = a(2 - x)$
38 $\dfrac{x^2}{m} = t$
39 $\dfrac{ax}{m} = n$
40 $\dfrac{e}{x} = p$

Homework 6F ⓒ

6.4 pages 277–279

a The number line shows the inequality $x > 3$
(the circle at 3 is not filled in).

b The number line shows the inequality $-2 < x \leqslant 2$
is shown (the circle at 2 is filled in).

1 Write the inequalities shown on the number lines, using the variable n.

a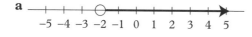

b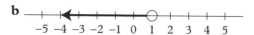

c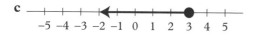

d

e

f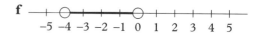

g

h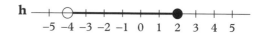

2 Show these inequalities on number lines.

a $x > 5$ **b** $x < 7$ **c** $x \geqslant -4$

d $x \leqslant -1$ **e** $x \geqslant 0$ **f** $1 < x < 6$

3 List all the whole number (or 'integer') solutions for these inequalities.

a $1 < x < 5$ **b** $0 < x \leqslant 5$ **c** $-2 \leqslant x < 2$

4 Solve these inequalities.

a $2x + 1 > 9$ **b** $5x - 1 < 16$ **c** $7x - 3 > 25$

d $\dfrac{5x - 1}{2} > 7$ **e** $\dfrac{2x + 1}{5} \geqslant 1$ **f** $3(x - 2) < 6$

5 Solve the inequality
$8 < x - 3 < 21$

6 Solve the inequality
$-1 < 2x + 1 < 9$

> Solve the two inequalities separately.

Homework 6G

6.5 pages 280–285

Reminders

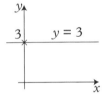
$y = 3$

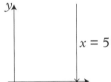
$x = 5$

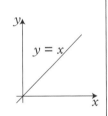
$y = x$

---

1 Write the coordinates of the points A, B, C, ... I.

2 Find the equation of the line which passes through the points

a A, G and F

b B and I

c D and H

d E and I

e D and G.

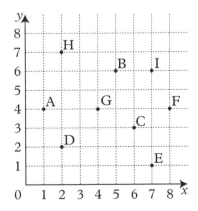

In questions **3** to **8** copy and complete the table and then draw the graph using a scale of 1 cm to 1 unit for both x and y.

3 $y = x + 3$

x	0	1	3	5
y	3			8

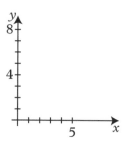

4 $y = 2x + 1$

x	0	1	2	3	4	5
y						

5 $y = 2x - 3$

x	0	1	2	3	4
y					

6 $y = 2(x + 2)$

x	0	1	2	3	4
y					

7 $y = 3x + 2$

x	−2	−1	0	1	2
y	−4				

8 $y = 2x - 1$

x	−2	−1	1	2	3
y					

9 a Draw the graph of $y = 2x - 1$ for values of x from 0 to 4.
  b Draw the graph of $y = x + 3$.
  c Write the coordinates of the point where the two lines meet.

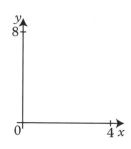

Homework 6H🅒

6.6 pages 286–289

The line $y = 2x + 1$ has gradient 2 and y-intercept 1.

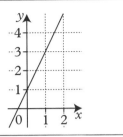

1 Find the gradients of AB, BC and AC.

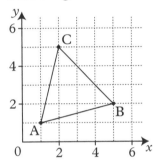

2 Find the gradients of DE, EF, FD.

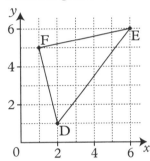

Write the equations of these lines.

3

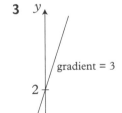

gradient = 3

4

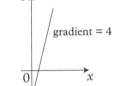

gradient = 4

5

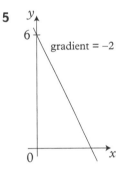

gradient = −2

6

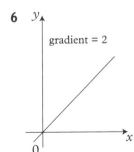

gradient = 2

7

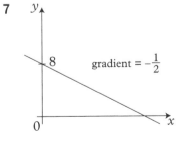

gradient = $-\frac{1}{2}$

8

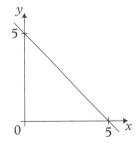

9 Find the gradient of the straight line through the points
   a $(2, 9)$ and $(4, 15)$ **b** $(1, -1)$ and $(3, 9)$.

10 (More difficult) Find the equation of the line which passes through
   the points $(0, 3)$ and $(2, 7)$.

Homework 6I 🔘

6.7 pages 290–292

1 The diagram shows the graphs of $x + y = 11$, $4x + y = 17$ and $x - 2y = 2$.

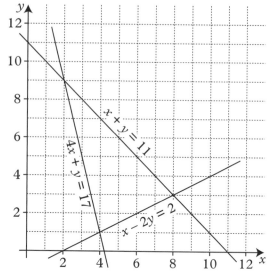

Use the graph to solve the simultaneous equations

a $x + y = 11$
   $x - 2y = 2$

b $4x + y = 17$
   $x + y = 11$

c $x - 2y = 2$
   $4x + y = 17$

2 a Draw the graphs of $x + 2y = 8$ and $x - y = 2$.
   Draw axes with x from 0 to 8.

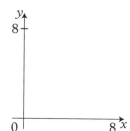

  b Use your graphs to solve the simultaneous equations
   $x + 2y = 8$
   $x - y = 2$

3 Solve the simultaneous equations

a $7x + 3y = 23$
   $x + y = 5$

b $4x + 7y = 26$
   $4x + 3y = 18$

Homework 6J 🔘

6.8 pages 296–301

1 Copy and complete the table for $y = x^2 - 3$.

x	-2	-1	0	1	2	3	4	5
x^2	4		0					
-3	-3	-3	-3					
y	1		-3					

2 Copy and complete the table for $y = x^2 + 2$.

x	-2	-1	0	1	2	3	4
x^2							
$+2$							
y							

3 Copy and complete the table for
$y = x^2 + 5x$.

x	−1	0	1	2	3	4	5	6
x^2								
+5x	−5	0	5					
y								

4 Copy and complete the table for
$y = x^2 + 3x$.

x	−3	−2	−1	0	1	2	3
x^2	9	4					
3x	−9	−6					
y	0	−2					

In questions **5** and **6** complete the table and then draw the graph.

5 Copy and complete the table for
$y = x^2 + x - 2$.

x	−3	−2	−1	0	1	2
x^2						
x	−3	−2				
−2	−2	−2	−2			
y						

Draw the graph of $y = x^2 + x - 2$,
using axes with x from −3 to +2 and
y from −3 to +4.

6 Copy and complete the table for
$y = x^2 + 3x + 1$.

x	−4	−3	−2	−1	0	1
x^2						
3x						
+1						
y						

Draw the graph of $y = x^2 + 3x + 1$,
using axes with x from −4 to +1 and
y from −2 to +5.

7 a Copy and complete the table for
$y = x^2 + 2x - 3$.

x	−4	−3	−2	−1	0	1	2
x^2	16						
2x	−8						
−3	−3	−3	−3				
y	5						

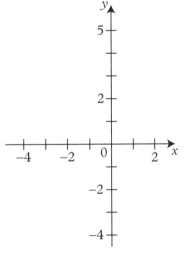

b Draw the graph of $y = x^2 + 2x - 3$, using axes with x
from −4 to +2 and y from −4 to +5.
c Use your graph to solve the equation $x^2 + 2x - 3 = 0$.
d By drawing a suitable line, use your graph to solve
the equation $x^2 + 2x - 3 = 2$.

7 Shape and space 2

Homework 7A Ⓒ

7.1 pages 306–307

On square grid paper draw the object and its image after reflection in the broken line.

1
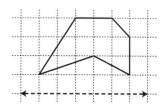

2
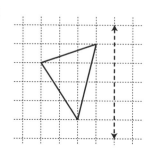

3
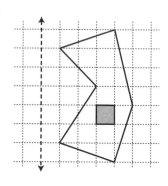

4
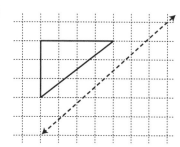

5
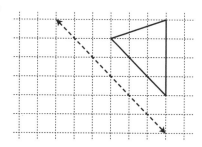

Draw the image of the given shape after reflection in line AB and then reflect this new shape in line XY.

6
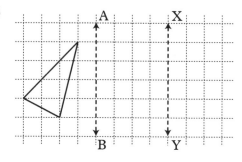

7
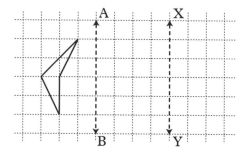

8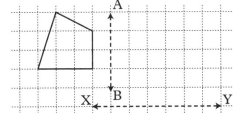

9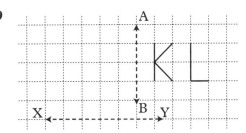

Homework 7B **7.1 pages 307–309**

1 Copy the diagram.
Draw the image of the triangle after reflection in
  a the x-axis; label it $\triangle 1$
  b the y-axis; label it $\triangle 2$
  c the line $x = 3$; label it $\triangle 3$.

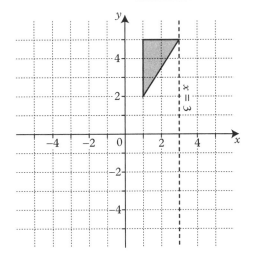

For questions **2** and **3** draw a pair of axes so that both x and y can take
values from -7 to $+7$.

2 a Plot and label $D(-6, 4)$, $E(-6, 7)$, $F(-4, 7)$.
  b Draw the lines $y = 3$ and $x = -2$. [Use dotted lines.]
  c Draw the image of $\triangle DEF$ after reflection in
    i the x-axis; label it $\triangle 1$.
    ii the y-axis; label it $\triangle 2$.
    iii the line $y = 3$; label it $\triangle 3$.
    iv the line $x = -2$; label it $\triangle 4$.
  d Write the coordinates of the image of point D in each case.

3 a Plot and label $A(-7, -6)$, $B(-7, -2)$, $C(-4, -2)$.
  b Draw the line $y = x$.
  c Reflect $\triangle ABC$ in the x-axis. Label the image $\triangle 1$.
  d Reflect $\triangle 1$ in the y-axis. Label the image $\triangle 2$.
  e Reflect $\triangle 2$ in the $y = x$. Label the image $\triangle 3$.

4 a Copy the diagram.
  b Reflect △DEF in the *x*-axis. Label the image △1.
  c Reflect △1 in the *y*-axis. Label the image △2.
  d Reflect △2 in the line *x* + *y* = 4. Label the image △3.
  e Write the coordinates of the right-angled vertex in △3.

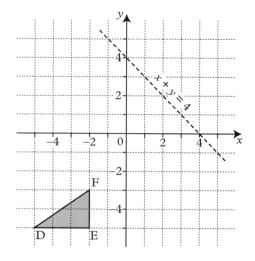

Homework 7C❻

7.1 pages 309–310

1 On square grid paper draw the object and its image under the rotation given.
Take O as the centre of rotation. Use tracing paper if possible.

a

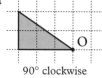

90° clockwise

b

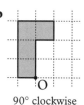

90° clockwise

c

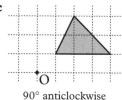

90° anticlockwise

2 Copy the diagram.
Rotate △ABC 90° clockwise about O and then rotate its image through 90° clockwise about P.

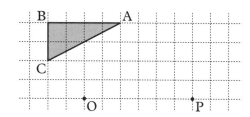

3 Copy the diagram.
Rotate ABCD through 90° anticlockwise about O and then reflect its image in the broken line.

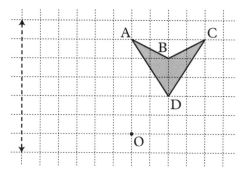

4 Copy the diagram.

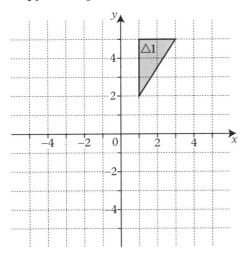

  a Rotate △1 180° about (0, 0) on to △2.
  b Rotate △2 90° clockwise about (0, −1) on to △3.
  c Rotate △3 180° about (0, 1) on to △4.
  d Describe fully the rotation which rotates △4 on to △1.

Homework 7D ⓒ

7.1 pages 316–318

Copy the diagrams on to square grid paper and then find the centre of enlargement by construction. (Leave space in your diagrams for the construction lines.)

1 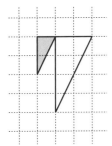   **2** 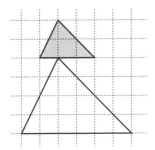   **3**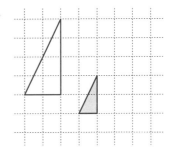

Copy the diagrams on to square grid paper and then draw an enlargement, using the scale factor given, with the point O as the centre of enlargement.

4 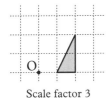   **5** 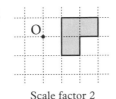   **6**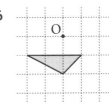

    Scale factor 3   Scale factor 2   Scale factor 3

For questions **7** and **8** draw a pair of axes with values from −7 to +7.

7 a Plot and label the triangles
  △1: (−5, 7), (−5, 4), (−6, 4)
  △2: (−6, −2), (−6, −4), (−5, −4)
  △3: (2, 6), (5, 6) (5, 5).

 b Draw the image of △1 after enlargement with scale factor 3, centre (−7, 7). Label the image △4.

 c Draw the image of △2 after enlargement with scale factor 2, centre (−7, −2). Label the image △5.

 d Draw the image of △3 after enlargement with scale factor 2, centre (4, 7). Label the image △6.

 e Write the coordinates of the 'pointed ends' of △4, △5 and △6.

8 a Plot and label the triangles
  △1: (4, 3), (7, 3), (7, 2)
  △2: (2, −2), (2, −5), (3, −5)
  △3: (−4, −2), (−7, −2), (−7, −3).

 b Draw the image of △1 after enlargement with scale factor 3, centre (7, 4). Label the image △4.

 c Draw the image of △2 after enlargement with scale factor 2, centre (4, −3). Label the image △5.

 d Draw the image of △3 after enlargement with scale factor 3, centre (−7, −5). Label the image △6.

 e Write the coordinates of the 'pointed ends' of △4, △5 and △6.

Homework 7E◉

7.1 pages 319–321

1 Write the vector for each of these translations.

For example △1 → △2 is $\begin{pmatrix} -1 \\ 3 \end{pmatrix}$.

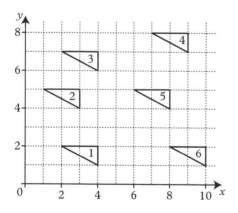

 a △1 → △5   **b** △2 → △3
 c △5 → △4   **d** △2 → △5
 e △3 → △5   **f** △6 → △2
 g △1 → △4   **h** △1 → △3

2 Copy this diagram.

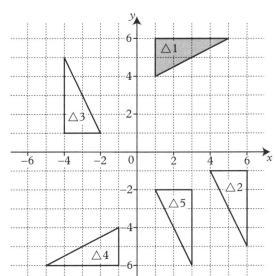

Describe fully these rotations.
a △1 → △2   **b** △1 → △3
c △1 → △4   **d** △1 → △5
[Given the angle, the direction and the centre.]

3 Copy this diagram.

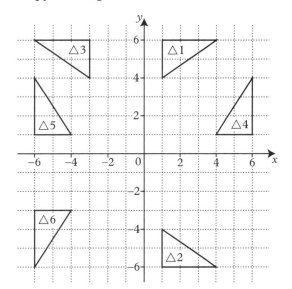

Describe fully these reflections.
a △1 → △2   **b** △1 → △3
c △1 → △4   **d** △4 → △5
e △5 → △6   **f** △2 → △5

4 Look at the diagram.
Describe fully each of these
transformations.
a △1 → △2
b △1 → △3
c △4 → △5
d △4 → △6

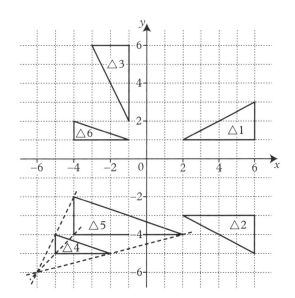

Homework 7F

7.2 pages 323–327

Circumference of a circle = πd
Area of a circle = πr^2

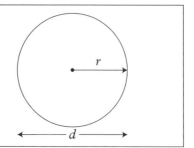

Give your answers to one decimal place.

1 Find the circumference of each circle.

a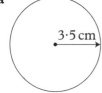
3·5 cm

b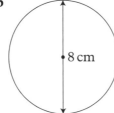
8 cm

c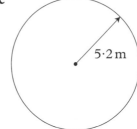
5·2 m

2 A circular plate has a diameter of 11 cm.
Calculate the circumference of the plate.

3 Calculate the area of each circle in question **1**.

4 a Draw a circle of radius 4·5 cm.
  b Draw a diameter on your circle.
  c Calculate the area of the circle.

5 A garden is made up of a rectangle
and a semicircle.
Calculate the total area of the garden.

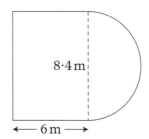
8·4 m
6 m

6 A square tile of side 20 cm has a circle of
diameter 20 cm drawn inside.
Calculate the area of the shaded region.

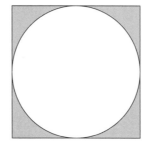

Homework 7G **C**

7.3 pages 328–331

The solids in questions **1** to **4** are made of one centimetre cubes.
Find the volume of each solid.

1   **2**   **3** 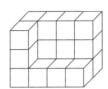   **4**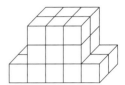

5 Find the volume of each cuboid.

a 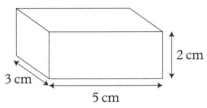   **b**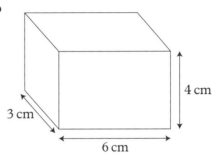

6 Copy and complete this table.

	l	*b*	*h*	*v*
a	4 cm	3 cm	2 cm	24 cm³
b	2·2 cm	5 cm	4 cm	
c	$1\frac{1}{2}$ m	2 m	5 m	
d	4 cm	2 cm		24 cm³
e	3 cm		5 cm	60 cm³
f		2·5 m	4 m	100 m³

7 A rectangular block of metal measuring 40 cm by 30 cm by 15 cm is
melted down and made into several identical blocks each measuring
6 cm by 5 cm by 3 cm. How many small blocks can be made?

8 The diagram shows an empty swimming pool.
Water is pumped into the pool at a rate of
2 m³ per minute. How long will it take to fill the pool?

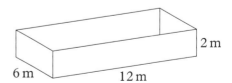

Homework 7HC

7.3 pages 332–335

> Volume of a prism   = (area of cross-section) × (length)
>
> Volume of a cylinder = $\pi r^2 h$

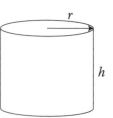

1 The cross-section of the prism in the
diagram is a right-angled triangle.
Find the volume of the prism.

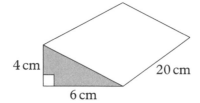

4 cm   6 cm   20 cm

Find the volume of each prism. All the angles are right angles and the
dimensions are in centimetres.

2

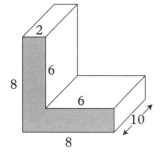

2
6
8
6
10
8

3

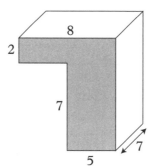

8
2
7
5
7

4

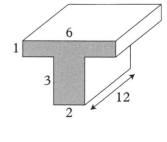

6
1
3
2
12

Find the volume of each cylinder, to the nearest whole number.

5

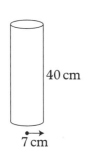

40 cm

7 cm

6

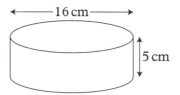

← 16 cm →

5 cm

7

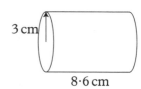

3 cm

8·6 cm

8 Which of these wooden rods is heavier, if they are made of the same sort of wood?

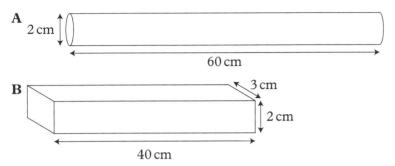

A 2 cm, 60 cm

B 3 cm, 2 cm, 40 cm

Homework 7I Ⓔ

7.4 pages 332–338

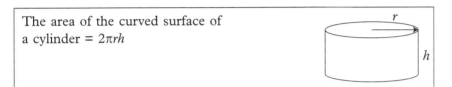

The area of the curved surface of a cylinder = $2\pi rh$

This homework contains questions on surface area and volume.

1 Calculate the curved surface area of each cylinder. All lengths are in cm.

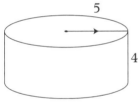

a 5, 4

b 6·2, 7·5

c 8, 11

2 Calculate the **total** surface area of a solid cylinder of radius 4 cm and height 8·4 cm.

3 Calculate the total surface area of each cuboid. All lengths are in cm.

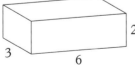

a 2, 3, 6

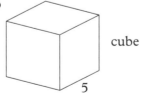

b cube, 5

4 The diagram shows a stack of boxes. End box is a cube of side 35 cm. Find the dimensions of this stack, giving your answer in **metres**.

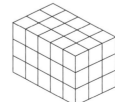

5 A cylindrical disc of radius 80 cm and thickness 1 cm is cut into eight identical pieces. Calculate the volume of one of the pieces. Make a drawing to show what one of the pieces would look like.

6 How many times can the cylindrical glass be filled from the large drum which is full of wine?

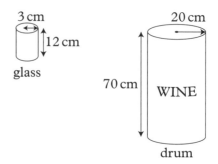

Homework 7J ⓒ

7.5 pages 338–339

1 The diagram shows the direction in which the aircraft, A, B, C and D, are flying from P. Find the bearing for each aircraft from P. (Remember that bearings are measured clockwise from north.)

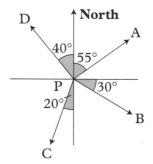

2 Here is a map of an island which has four main towns. Use a protractor to measure
  a the bearing of C from A
  b the bearing of D from A
  c the bearing of B from A
  d the bearing of C from D
  e the bearing of D from B.

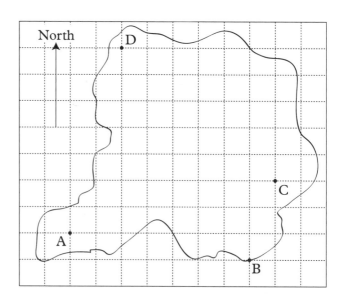

3 A ship sails 8 km due north and then
a further 7 km on a bearing 080°.
a Make a scale drawing using a scale
of 1 cm to represent 1 km.
b Find the distance of the ship from
its starting point.

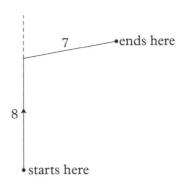

4 A plane flies 700 km on a bearing 070° and then a further 1000 km
on a bearing 150°.
Make a scale drawing of the flight and find how far the plane
is from its starting point.

Homework 7K ⊙

7.6 pages 341–346

The sum of the exterior angles for any
polygon is 360°.
$$a + b + c + d + e + f = 360°$$

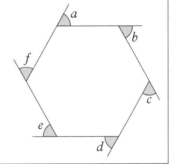

1 The diagram shows a regular hexagon
with its exterior angles marked.
Calculate the size of each exterior angle.

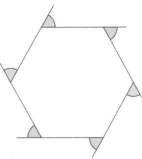

2 Find the angles x and y in this pentagon.

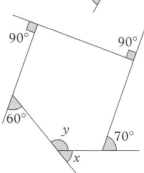

3 The diagram shows part of
a **regular** polygon.
How many sides does
the polygon have?

4 The diagram shows a regular polygon P
with two regular hexagons and a square.
Find the angle *a*.

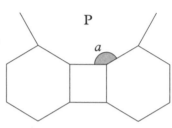

5 The diagram shows squares and
equilateral triangles joined together.
Find the angle *b*.

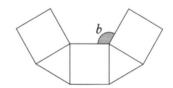

Homework 7L●

7.7 pages 346–348

You need a pencil, a ruler and a pair of compasses.

1 Draw two points A and B, 8 cm apart.
Draw the locus of points which are
equidistant from A and B.

2 a Draw triangle PQR on square
grid paper.
b Construct the locus of points
which are equidistant from lines
PQ and PR (that is, the bisector
of angle P).
c Construct the perpendicular
bisector of PR.

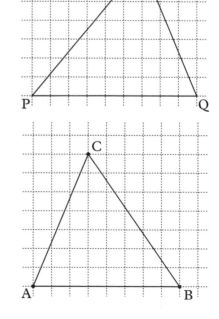

3 Triangle ABC is a scale drawing
of a garden in which the side of
one square = 1 m. Copy the diagram
on to square grid paper.
a Construct the bisector of angle B.
b Mike puts a post in the garden.
He wants the post to be nearer
to line AB than to line AC.
He also wants the post to be
within 5 m of C. Shade the
region where the post can be.

4 The diagram shows the
walls of a shed, in which the side of
one square = 1 m. A dog is attached by
a rope 5 m long to the point P on
the wall.

Draw a diagram on square
grid paper and shade the
region that the dog can reach.

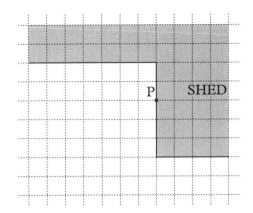

Homework 7M🄒

7.8 pages 349–351

Use Pythagoras' theorem to find x.
$x^2 = 3^2 + 7^2$
$x^2 = 9 + 49 = 58$
$x = \sqrt{58} = 7 \cdot 62$ (to 3 sf)

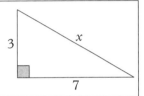

In questions **1** to **4** find the side marked with a letter. All lengths are
in cm. Give answers correct to 3 sf, where necessary.

1

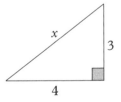

2

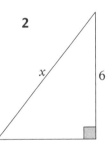

3

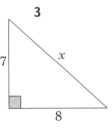

4

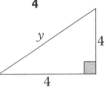

5 Copy and complete.
$a^2 + 5^2 = 9^2$
$a^2 + 25 = 81$
$\quad a^2 = 81 - \square = \square$

$\quad a = \sqrt{\square} = \square$

In questions **6** to **9** find the side marked with a letter.

6

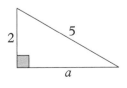

7

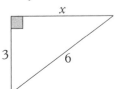

8

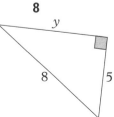

9

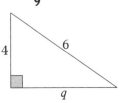

10 A rectangle measures 8 cm by 5 cm. Calculate the length of the diagonals of the rectangle.

11 A ship sails 9 km due north and then a further 17 km due east. How far is the ship from its starting point?

Homework 7N◉

7.8 pages 351–353

1 A rectangle of length 10 cm has diagonals of length 12 cm.
Calculate the width of the rectangle.

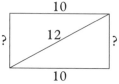

2 A rectangle of width 6·5 cm has diagonals of length 10 cm. Calculate the length of the rectangle.

3 In the diagram PQ = 2·35 cm, PR = 9·5 cm and RS = 4·2 cm. Calculate the length of QS.

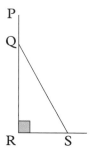

4 Calculate the length x.

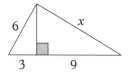

5 Calculate the length y.

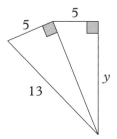

6 a Draw an equilateral triangle of side 8 cm and draw a line of symmetry.
   b Calculate the height of the triangle.
   c Calculate the area of the triangle.

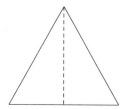

8   Handling data 2

Homework 8A Ⓒ

8.1 pages 366–370

1 Look at these diagrams.

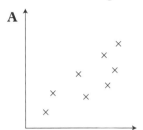

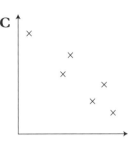

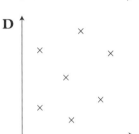

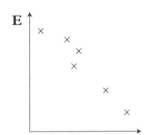

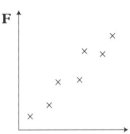

Which diagrams show
a no correlation   **b** positive correlation   **c** negative correlation?

2 Here are the heights and
masses of 9 people.
  a Draw the axes shown
     and complete the
     scatter graph.
  b Describe the
     correlation (if any)
     which the diagram
     shows.

Name	Mass (kg)	Height (cm)
Alan	45	115
Ben	60	160
Phil	65	155
Lucy	55	125
Henry	75	160
Harry	75	170
Dick	65	140
Spike	85	180
Sam	52	146

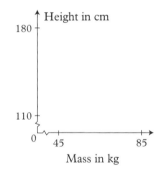

3 Plot the points given on a scatter graph, with x across the page and y
up the page. Draw axes with values from 0 to 20.
Describe the correlation, if any, between the values of x and y.
(for example, 'strong positive', 'weak negative' etc.)

a

x	4	14	10	20	18	8	4	8
y	14	8	6	2	4	16	20	10

b

x	10	10	4	6	8	14	14	12	9
y	12	14	4	6	10	18	16	14	10

c If there is correlation, draw a line of best fit through the points you
have plotted.

Homework 8B

8.2 pages 370–372

1 The table shows pulse rates and weights of an under 16s football team.

Weight (kg)	30	35	40	55	85	75	60	65	85	82	62
Pulse (beats/min)	55	80	91	80	52	60	51	70	51	94	89

a Copy and complete the scatter graph to show the data.

b Describe the correlation in the scatter graph.

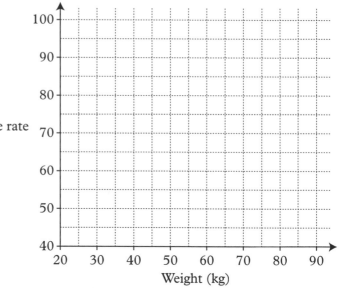

2 The table shows the heights and weights of eight students.

Weight (kg)	35	65	71	45	50	30	83	75
Height (cm)	150	170	178	160	167	155	180	177

a Draw a scatter graph to show the data in the table.

b Describe the correlation.

c Draw a line of best fit.

d Another student is 166 cm tall. Use your line of best fit to estimate that student's likely weight.

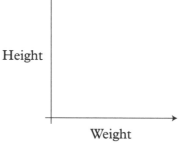

3 Describe the correlation in each diagram.

a

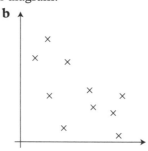

b

c

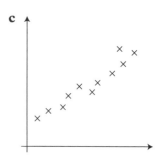

Homework 8C

8.2 pages 370–372

1 A survey about smoking was conducted. The results are shown in the two-way table.

	Smoker	Non-smoker	Total
Male		210	400
Female			
Total		525	1000

  a Copy and complete the table.
  b How many female smokers were there?

2 500 people raised money for charity by performing various idiotic acts. The results are shown in the two-way table.

	Sky dive	Head shaved	Bathed in baked beans	Total
Loved doing it		64	33	
Said afterwards, 'I must have been mad'				232
Total	225	170		500

  a Copy and complete the two-way table.
  b One person is picked at random. Find the probability
    that that person
    i said afterwards 'I must have been mad'
    ii did the sky dive and loved it.

3 Students at a school were asked who they thought would win the next Football World Cup. Here are the results:

B = Boy, G = Girl, A = Argentina, E = England, S = Scotland

B, A	B, S	B, S	G, A	B, S	B, S	B, A	B, S
G, E	G, S	B, A	G, E	G, S	G, S	B, S	G, S
B, S	B, S	G, S	B, S	B, A	B, S	G, S	G, S

  a Record the results in a two-way table.
  b How many girls said that England would win?
  c What percentage of the girls said that Argentina
    would win?
  d In which country do you think the survey
    was taken?

Homework 8D

8.2 pages 370–372

1 Here are 12 shapes.

Copy and complete the two-way table.

	Shaded	Unshaded
Squares		
Circles		

2 The employees in an office stated when they would like to have
an extra day's holiday.
Here are the results.

M = Male, F = Female
C = Christmas, S = Summer, A = Autumn

M, S	F, C	F, C	F, C
F, C	F, A	M, S	M, A
M, S	M, S	F, S	F, A
M, A	F, C	F, S	F, C

  a Record the results in a two-way table.
  b How many employees were females?
  c What percentage of the females chose Christmas?

3 This incomplete two-way table shows details of
six-year-olds who can swim or who cannot swim.

	Girls	Boys	Total
Can swim		80	150
Cannot swim	160		
Total			500

  a Copy and complete the table.
  b What percentage of the boys can swim?
     Give your answer to 1 dp.
  c What percentage of those who cannot swim are girls?

Homework 8E ⓒ

8.5 pages 383–385

1 A road traffic survey recorded the number of cars passing a certain place in 5-minute intervals. Here are the results.

4	10	14	1	14	25	36	13	24	16
18	7	10	27	35	19	20	22	12	28
15	23	8	13	27	5	17	38	23	14

For convenience the data is recorded in a table.
Copy and complete the table.

Number of cars	Tally	Frequency
0–9		
10–19		
20–29		
30–39		

2 The manager of a restaurant wanted to find out from customers what they thought of their last meal.
He used this question on a questionnaire.

What did you think of your last meal?
Excellent ☐   Very Good ☐   Good ☐

a What do you think is wrong with this question?
b Write a similar question which is better than the one he asked.

3 Shaleeza is conducting a survey about renting DVDs.
Here is one of her questions.

How many DVDs did you rent last year?
☐   ☐   ☐
0–10   10–20   20–30

What two things are wrong with this question?

9 Number 3

Homework 9A C

9.1 pages 390–392

1 Copy and complete the table which shows equivalent fractions, decimals and percentages.

	Fraction	Decimal	Percentage
a	$\frac{17}{100}$	0.17	17%
b	☐	0.34	☐
c	$\frac{3}{4}$	☐	☐
d	☐	☐	4%

2 Here are some fractions.

$\frac{1}{50}$	$\frac{7}{11}$	$\frac{5}{25}$	$\frac{2}{5}$

Select one that is
a equal to 0·4   **b** equal to 2%
c equal to $\frac{1}{5}$ **d** greater than 50%

3 Write these numbers in order of size, smallest first.
0·7   0·07   0·67   0·617   0·716

4 Find the missing numbers so that the answer is always 40.

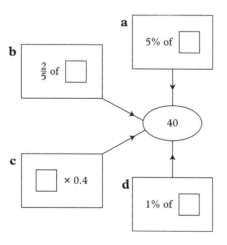

5 Stevie and Dean share a prize in the ratio 2 : 3.
What percentage of the prize does Dean receive?

Homework 9B

9.2 pages 392–394

Remember these formulae.

Distance = Speed × Time

$$\text{Speed} = \frac{\text{Distance}}{\text{Time}}$$

$$\text{Time} = \frac{\text{Distance}}{\text{Speed}}$$

$$\frac{D}{S \times T}$$

1 How far will a car travel in 2 h, if it has a constant speed of 60 km/h?

2 An athlete ran for 50 m at a constant speed. If it took him 5 s, what was his speed?

3 A slow vehicle, which can maintain a steady speed of 11 km/h, has to travel a distance of 44 km.
How long will it take?

4 A high-speed train travels for 3 h at a constant speed of 200 km/h. How far does the train go in this time?

5 A cyclist takes 4 h to travel 48 km. If he travelled at a fixed speed, find that speed.

6 How far will a car travel in 3 s, given that it is going at a steady speed of 15 m/s?

7 A train travels from London to Newcastle in 3 hours 15 minutes. Given that the distance is 280 miles, calculate the average speed of the train in miles per hour.

8 A plane took 2 hours 30 minutes to fly 235 miles. Calculate, in miles per hour, the average speed of the plane.

9 A driver makes two journeys.

Journey	Average speed	Time
York to Oxford	60 mph	3 hours
York to Dover	52 mph	4 hours 45 minutes

Calculate the difference in the length of these two journeys.

Homework 9C

9.3 pages 395–396

$$4500 = 4\cdot5 \times 1000 = 4\cdot5 \times 10^3 \qquad 0\cdot00042 = 4\cdot2 \times 10^{-4}$$
$$640 = 6\cdot4 \times 10^2 \qquad\qquad\qquad 0\cdot005 = 5 \times 10^{-3}$$

A Rewrite these numbers in standard form.

1 3200	**2** 18 000	**3** 4300	**4** 580
5 700 000	**6** 2600	**7** 48	**8** 27 000
9 650 000	**10** 30 000	**11** 2 500 000	**12** 800
13 13	**14** 2000	**15** 624 000	**16** 20 million
17 0·026	**18** 0·007	**19** 0·000 012	**20** 0·000 352
21 0·000 001 67	**22** 0·0009	**23** 0·002 58	**24** 0·434
25 0·0211	**26** 0·000 000 805	**27** 0·319	**28** 0·002 08
29 0·000 46	**30** 0·000 01	**31** 0·000 000 27	**32** 0·000 000 018 3

B In this exercise there are 40 numbers written in standard form.
Rewrite them as ordinary numbers.

1 $2\cdot4 \times 10^2$	**2** $3\cdot6 \times 10^3$	**3** $1\cdot9 \times 10^4$	**4** $8\cdot3 \times 10^3$
5 $7\cdot5 \times 10^2$	**6** $4\cdot8 \times 10^5$	**7** $9\cdot2 \times 10^3$	**8** $6\cdot3 \times 10^1$
9 $7\cdot2 \times 10^4$	**10** $2\cdot6 \times 10^5$	**11** 7×10^{-2}	**12** 8×10^{-1}
13 2×10^{-5}	**14** $4\cdot7 \times 10^{-4}$	**15** $2\cdot13 \times 10^{-2}$	**16** $1\cdot72 \times 10^{-3}$
17 $6\cdot6 \times 10^{-1}$	**18** $4\cdot9 \times 10^{-2}$	**19** 4×10^{-1}	**20** $8\cdot3 \times 10^{-3}$

Homework 9D

9.3 pages 397–398

$$(2 \times 10^4) \times (3 \times 10^5) \ = (2 \times 3) \times 10^{(4+5)} = 6 \times 10^9$$
$$(8 \times 10^5) \times (2 \times 10^{-3}) = (8 \times 2) \times 10^{5-3} \ = 16 \times 10^2 = 1\cdot6 \times 10^3$$
$$(9 \times 10^8) \div (3 \times 10^2) = (9 \div 3) \times 10^{8-2} \ = 3 \times 10^6$$

Work out these, giving your answers in standard form.

1 $(3 \times 10^2) \times (2 \times 10^1)$	**2** $(4 \times 10^3) \times (2 \times 10^1)$	**3** $(4 \times 10^1) \times (1 \times 10^6)$
4 $(8 \times 10^3) \times (2 \times 10^4)$	**5** $(7 \times 10^2) \times (4 \times 10^{-3})$	**6** $(5 \times 10^3) \times (7 \times 10^{-1})$
7 $(6 \times 10^2) \times (6 \times 10^{-1})$	**8** $(4 \times 10^{-2}) \times (3 \times 10^{-1})$	**9** $(8 \times 10^7) \div (2 \times 10^3)$
10 $(7 \times 10^5) \times (1 \times 10^2)$	**11** $(6 \times 10^2) \div (3 \times 10^{-1})$	**12** $(7 \times 10^2) \div (5 \times 10^{-1})$

13 a To work out $(1\cdot75 \times 10^2) \times (3 \times 10^9)$, using a calculator,
press these buttons.

The answer is $5\cdot25 \times 10^{11}$.

b To work out $(8 \times 10^4) \div (2 \times 10^{-3})$, press these buttons

| 8 | EXP | 4 | ÷ | 2 | EXP | − | 3 | = |

The answer is 40 000 000 or 4×10^7.

Work out these, giving your answers in standard form.

14 $(7 \cdot 2 \times 10^2) \times (3 \times 10^1)$ **15** $(3 \cdot 5 \times 10^2) \times (7 \times 10^4)$ **16** $(6 \cdot 7 \times 10^5) \times (4 \times 10^7)$

17 $(2 \cdot 9 \times 10^2) \times (2 \times 10^1)$ **18** $(4 \cdot 8 \times 10^{-1}) \times (8 \times 10^6)$ **19** $(1 \cdot 75 \times 10^3) \div (5 \times 10^1)$

20 $(3 \cdot 72 \times 10^2) \times (6 \times 10^2)$ **21** $(1 \cdot 72 \times 10^2) \div (4 \times 10^{-1})$ **22** $(1 \cdot 3 \times 10^4) \div (2 \times 10^2)$

23 $(2 \cdot 45 \times 10^2) \div (5 \times 10^{-1})$

24 Given that $x = 4 \times 10^7$ and $y = 3 \times 10^4$, work out

     a xy **b** $\dfrac{y}{x}$ **c** x^2

25 A pile of 20 000 sheets of paper is $1 \cdot 6$ metres high. Work out the thickness of one sheet of paper in metres, writing your answer in standard form.

Homework 9E ⒸⒸ

9.4 pages 399–403

10 mm = 1 cm	1000 g = 1 kg	1000 ml = 1 litre
100 cm = 1 m	1000 kg = 1 t (t for tonne)	
1000 m = 1 km		

Copy and complete.

1 3 m = ☐ cm   **2** 2·8 km = ☐ m   **3** 3·2 m = ☐ cm   **4** 3 kg = ☐ g

5 400 m = ☐ km   **6** 250 cm = ☐ m   **7** 3 t = ☐ kg   **8** 20 cm = ☐ mm

9 5000 ml = ☐ litres   **10** 3400 g = ☐ kg   **11** 1·2 t = ☐ kg   **12** 260 g = ☐ kg

13 Choose the unit that would be best for measuring

     a the weight of a teaspoon

     b the length of a room

     c the distance from Bristol to London

     d the capacity of the petrol tank of a car

     e the width of this book.

12 inches = 1 foot	16 ounces = 1 pound	8 pints = 1 gallon
3 feet = 1 yard	14 pounds = 1 stone	
1760 yards = 1 mile		

Copy and complete.

14 2 feet = ☐ inches   **15** 6 feet = ☐ yards   **16** 16 pints = ☐ gallons

17 1 pound = ☐ ounces   **18** 36 inches = ☐ feet   **19** 2 pound = ☐ ounces

20 1 yard = ☐ inches   **21** 1 stone = ☐ pounds   **22** 10 gallons = ☐ pints

23 Write a sensible imperial unit to measure
  a the height of a room
  b the capacity of a large bottle of cola
  c the weight of a lorry
  d the diameter of a DVD.

Homework 9F ⓒ

9.4 pages 399–403

> 1 inch ≈ 2·5 cm   1 gallon ≈ 5 litres
>
> 1 kg ≈ 2 pounds   1 km ≈ $\frac{5}{8}$ mile (or 8 km ≈ 5 miles)

1 Copy the statements and answer 'true' or 'false'.
  a 16 km is about 10 miles
  b 25 cm is about 10 inches
  c 5 kg of meat is about 10 pounds
  d 3 gallons of petrol is about 20 litres.

2 Copy and complete these. (≈ means 'is approximately')
  a 10 cm ≈ ☐ inches   **b** 20 litres ≈ ☐ gallons   **c** 2 kg ≈ ☐ pounds

  d 20 gallons ≈ ☐ litres   **e** 50 miles ≈ ☐ km   **f** 1 foot ≈ ☐ cm

3 Copy and complete this table. Write a sensible unit for each
  measurement.

		Metric	Imperial
a	The distance from York to Portsmouth		
b	The weight of a table		
c	The capacity of a bucket		
d	The length of a football pitch		
e	The thickness of this book		

4 The scale shows pints and litres.
  a Estimate how many litres there are in 1 pint.
  b Estimate the number of pints in 10 litres.
  c Copy and complete.
    3 pints = ☐ litres, correct to 1 decimal place.

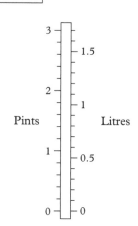

Homework 9G

9.5 pages 403–405

> If the height of a glass is 13 cm, correct to the nearest centimetre, the actual height could be from 12·5 cm to 13·5 cm.
>
> 12.5 cm   13 cm   13.5 cm

1 Meera's handspan is 18 cm, to the nearest centimetre. Write down her greatest possible handspan.

2 The diameter of a saucepan is 20 cm, correct to the nearest cm. What is the least possible diameter of the saucepan?

3 The length of a car journey is 13 km, to the nearest km. What is the greatest possible length of the journey?

4 The diagram shows a weighing scale.

   a Which letter is at $4\frac{1}{2}$ kg?

   b A cake is weighed at 2·5 kg, correct to the nearest 0·1 kg. What is the greatest possible weight of the cake?

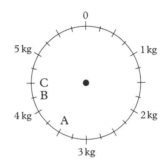

5 Copy and complete the table for each measurement.
   a Steve's height = 162 cm, to nearest cm
   b Steve's weight = 53 kg, to nearest kg
   c Length of envelope = 21·6 cm, to nearest 0·1 cm
   d Volume of glass = 0·8 litres, to nearest 0·1 litre
   e Length of field = 260 m, to nearest 10 m

Lower limit	Upper limit
	162·5 cm

6 The mass of a butterfly is 3·14 g, correct to the nearest 0·01 gram. Write the greatest and least possible mass of the butterfly.

10 Probability

Homework 10A

10.2 pages 418–426

1 Mark chooses a ball at random from a bag
containing a blue ball, a white ball,
a yellow ball and a green ball. Write the
probability that the ball Mark chooses is
a white   **b** blue   **c** green.

2 Tony rolls a fair dice. Write the chance of him getting
  a a 5   **b** a 3   **c** an even number.

3 Joy selects one card at random from the nine cards shown.
Find the probability that Joy selects
  a the ace of diamonds   **b** a king
  c the 8 of spades   **d** a heart or a diamond.

4 Tom throws a fair dice once. What is the probability that Tom gets
  a a 4   **b** an even number   **c** a number less than 3?

5 Max puts cards numbered 2, 3, 4, 5, 6, 7, 8, 9, 10, 11, 12 and 13 in a
box. Simon selects one card at random. Find the probability that
Simon selects
  a a 10   **b** an odd number   **c** a prime number
  d a square number   **e** a number greater than 7   **f** a number less than 15.

6 Rana puts cards lettered A, B, C, D, E, F, G, H, I, J and K
in a box.
She selects one card at random. Find the probability that
Rana selects
  a a D   **b** an I or a J
  c a vowel   **d** a consonant.

7 Rashid writes each letter of the word 'PARALLEL' on a card and places
the 8 cards in a box. He selects one card.
Find the probability that Rashid selects
  a an A   **b** a P
  c an L   **d** an R or an E.

Homework 10B

10.2 pages 426–427

1 A dice has faces numbered 1, 2, 3, 3, 3 and 6. Find the probability of rolling
   a a 2   **b** an odd number.

2 Jo selects one ball from a box which contains 3 red balls, 2 yellow balls
  and 4 blue balls.

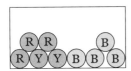

  Find the probability that she selects
  a a red ball   **b** a blue ball   **c** a yellow ball.

3 a A bag contains 5 green balls, 2 yellow balls and 4 red balls.
    Find the probability of selecting
    i a green ball   **ii** a yellow ball.
  b The 2 yellow balls are removed and replaced by 1 red ball and 1 white ball.
    Find the probability of selecting
    i a green ball   **ii** a white ball
    iii a red ball   **iv** a yellow ball.

4 a Rob puts these numbered balls in a bag.
    He takes out one ball.
    Find the probability that Rob selects a ball numbered 4.
  b Rob puts more balls into the bag so that the chance of
    getting a 5 is **twice** the chance of getting a 2.
    What balls could he put in the bag?

5 The numbers of occupants of the houses in one street
  are shown on this chart.
  Find the probability that one house, chosen at
  random, will have
  a three occupants
  b five occupants
  c no occupants
  d more than four occupants
  e less than three occupants.

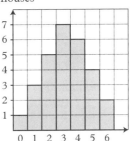

6 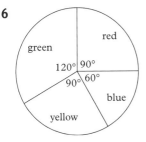 The pie chart shows the colour of the cars in
  a car park. Find the probability that one car,
  chosen at random
  a is red
  b is blue
  c is yellow
  d is green
  e is either red or yellow.

Homework 10C⊙

10.2 pages 426–427

1 Here is a spinner with 6 equal sectors.
a What is the probability of spinning a 5?
b Say whether the following statement is true or false.
Explain why.
'If you make six spins you are bound to
get at least one 4.'

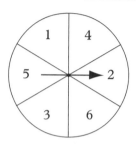

2 Jack writes each letter of the word 'COMPREHENSIVE' on a card and
places the cards in a box. One card is selected. Find the probability
that the card is
a an E   **b** a P   **c** a vowel   **d** a consonant.

3 Katie puts balls numbered 1, 2, 3, 4, . . . 30 in a bag. She selects one ball
at random. Find the probability that she selects
a a 5
b a multiple of 5
c a number less than 10
d a prime number
e a square number
f a number greater than 40.

4 A bag contains a number of red, green and yellow balls.
When a ball is chosen at random, the probability that it
is green is 0·2.
There are 25 balls in the bag. How many of the balls are green?

5 A fair dice is rolled 60 times. How many times would you expect to roll
a a 1   **b** an even number?

6 This spinner is spun 40 times. How many times
would you except to spin
a an 8
b a number less than 3?

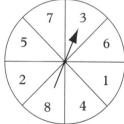

7 The pie chart shows the nationality of the children in a hotel.
Find the probability that one child, chosen at random
a is British
b is German
c is French
d is Italian
e is British or German.

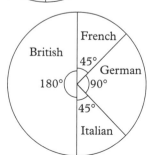

Homework 10D ⓒ

10.2 pages 426–427

1 A coin is biased so that the probability of tossing a head is 0·6. How many heads would you expect when the coin is tossed 100 times?

2 One card is selected from these cards. This is done 50 times.

    a How many times would you expect to get the three of diamonds?

    b How many times would you expect to get a 2?

3 Susie selects one card from a full pack of 52 playing cards. Find the probability that Susie selects

    a an ace   **b** the jack of hearts   **c** a picture card (not aces)

    d a red card   **e** a black ace   **f** a 10 or 9.

4 A coin is biased so that the chance of getting heads is twice the chance of getting tails. What is the probability of getting tails?

5 Luke tosses a 10p coin and a 20p coin at the same time. Make a list of all the possible ways in which they could land.

6 Harry throws a coin and a dice. He could get a head and a 2 (H, 2). Make a list of the 12 possible outcomes.

7 Here are two bags containing balls. From which bag is the probability of selecting a white ball greater? (You may use a calculator.)

                                            4 white   7 white

                                            7 black   13 black

Homework 10E ©

10.3 pages 428–431

1 Sarah tosses three coins (10p, 20p, 50p) together.
   a Make a list of all the possible outcomes.
   b What is the probability that Sarah gets three tails?

2 You can choose from 4 possible drinks.

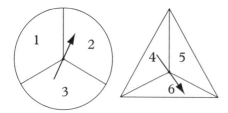

| tea | coffee | orange | water |

I buy a drink for myself and one for my brother.
Make a list of all the possible pairs of drinks I could get.

3 These two spinners are spun at the same time.
The diagram shows a 2 and a 6 to give a total of 8.

   a Copy and complete this table to
   show all the possible outcomes
   and totals.
   b Find the probability of getting
   a total of 6.

+	4	5	6
1			
2			8
3			

4 A red dice and a white dice are rolled
together and the scores are added
to give a total.
   a Copy and complete this table
   to show all the outcomes.
   b Find the probability of getting
   a total of 4.
   c Find the probability of getting
   a total of 6.

+	1	2	3	4	5	6
1						
2			5			
3						9
4						
5						
6						

Homework 10F C

10.4 pages 432–434

1 A coin is biased so that the probability of getting a head is 0·45. What is the probability of getting a tail?

2 A box contains 12 balls: 3 red, 2 yellow, 4 green and 3 white.

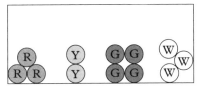

Find the probability of selecting
a a red ball   **b** a ball which is not red
c a yellow ball   **d** a ball which is not yellow.

3 In a football match the probability of Chelsea winning is 0·7 and the probability of Chelsea drawing is 0·2. What is the probability of Chelsea losing?

4 A bag contains balls which are either red, white or blue.
The probability of selecting a red ball is 0·3.
The probability of selecting a white ball is 0·35.
a Find the probability of selecting a blue ball.
b Find the probability of selecting a ball which is not blue.

5 The table shows the probabilities of four people of winning in their next game of golf.

Jane	Susy	Samithra	Deepa
0·3	0·25	x	0·15

a What is the probability of either Susy or Deepa winning?
b What is the probability of Samithra winning?
c What is the probability of Jane **not** winning?

6 Twenty-one people in a survey were asked which party they intended to vote for in the next election.

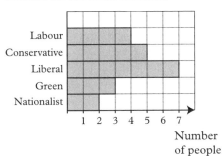

Find the probability that one person, chosen at random
a will vote Liberal   **b** will vote Labour
c will not vote Conversative   **d** will vote either Green or Nationalist.

11 Using and applying mathematics

Homework 11A◉ Mixed problems

1 Work out $5 \times (7 - 4)^2$.

2 Ahmed doubles a number, then adds it to 26 and the answer is 40.
Find Ahmed's number.

3 Find the angles marked with letters.

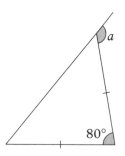

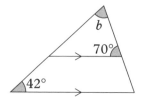

4 The perimeter of a basketball court is 86 m. If the length of the court is
28 m, what is the width?

5 Calculate the shaded area.
ABCD is a rectangle.
The lengths are in cm.

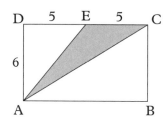

6 Work out 55% of £130.

7 It takes Emerson 23 minutes to walk to school. At what time must he
leave home to arrive at school at 8:45 a.m?

8 A wooden rod is 2 m long. Four pieces, each 33 cm long, are cut from
the rod. How much is left?

9 Solve the equation.
$3x - 1 = x + 11$

10 Work out.
$\dfrac{1}{5} + \dfrac{1}{2}$

Homework 11B

1 Jolene thinks of a number, divides it by 2 and adds 5.
The answer is 11. What is Jolene's number?

2 Round these numbers to the nearest whole number.
   a 11·204   **b** 210·45   **c** 1·82

3 Sid got 17 marks out of a possible 20. What percentage was that?

4 Copy and complete the table.

Fraction	Decimal	Percentage
	0·4	
$\frac{1}{10}$		
		15%

5 A car travels 301 km on 8 litres of petrol. Find the number of km per
litre, correct to one decimal place.

6 Copy and complete the table below. (H.C.F. means 'highest common
factor'.)

	1st number	2nd number	Factors of 1st number (in any order)	Factors of 2nd number (in any order)	Common factors (in any order)	H.C.F.
a	8	12	1, 8, 2, 4	1, 12, 2, 6, 3, 4	1, 2, 4	4
b	14	21	__, __, __, __	__, __, __, __	__, __	
c	6	15	__, __, __, __	__, __, __, __	__, __	
d	16	24	__, __, __, __, __	__, __, __, __, __, __, __, __	__, __, __, __	
e	15	25	__, __, __, __	__, __, __	__, __	
f	22	33	__, __, __, __	__, __, __, __	__, __	

7 Eight litres of paint cost £44. What is the cost of 11 litres
of paint?

8 Work out.
   a $-1 + 7$ **b** $-3 - 8$ **c** $10 - 22$ **d** $(-3) \times 4$

Homework 11C

Draw a copy of this crossnumber pattern. Complete the puzzle using a calculator. Where there are decimals, put the point on the line between squares.

Across

1 $3^2 + 4^2 + 5^2 + 6^2$

2 $\sqrt{2}$ (to 3 sf)

3 $3 \times 4 \times 6^2$

5 $\sqrt{20}$ (to 3 sf)

7 $\dfrac{9 \times 1\cdot5}{7 - 6\cdot9}$

9 $(71 - 47)^2$

10 $2\cdot07^2$ (to 2 sf)

11 $\dfrac{41 \times 4}{20}$

12 $\dfrac{20 \times 19 \times 18}{2 \times 2 \times 5}$

14 $(8 \times 7) + (6 \times 8)$

16 $\dfrac{36^2}{6}$

17 $5 \times 4 \times 3 \times 2 \times 1$

Down

1 $9\cdot2^2$ (to 3 sf)

4 $1\cdot295^3$ (to 3 sf)

6 $14 - 6\cdot97$

8 $60^2 + 30$

9 $2\cdot4^2 \times 5\cdot76 + 18\cdot8224$

10 $6\cdot48^2$ (to 2 sf)

11 $52\cdot8 + 31\cdot4$

13 $\dfrac{5 \times 6 \times 7 \times 8}{4} + (3 \times 7)$

14 $\dfrac{800}{7 + 25 + 18}$

15 $\dfrac{11\cdot18^2}{12\cdot5}$ (to 2 sf)

Homework 11D

1 An athlete started a training run at 11:15 and finished at 13:05. How long had she been running, in hours and minutes?

2 A square has an area of $20\cdot25 \text{ cm}^2$. Calculate its perimeter.

3 The bill for 5 people in a restaurant is £31·80. Find the cost per person correct to the nearest pound.

4 Calculate the area of this shape.

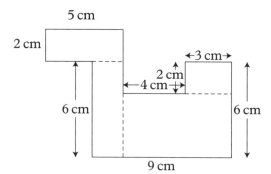

5 A map uses a scale of 1 to 1000.

  a Calculate the actual length, in metres, of a road which is 5 cm long on the map.

  b A lake is 800 m long. Calculate, in centimetres, the length of the lake on the map.

6 A shop buys cans of drink at £7.20 for 48 cans and sells them at 17p per can. Calculate the profit on one can.

7 How many seconds are there in 3 days?

8 How many stamps each costing 14p can be bought for £2?

9 Find the angles marked with letters.

a
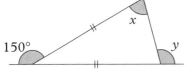

b
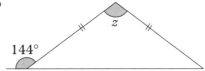

10 Amongst other ingredients you need 240 g of butter and 2 teaspoons of sugar to make 6 scones.
a What weight of butter do you need to make 30 scones?
b How many teaspoons of sugar do you need to make 9 scones?

Homework 11E **C**

1 Screws are sold in packets of eight and I need 182 screws for a job. How many packets must I buy and how many screws will be left over?

2 What number, when divided by 7 and then multiplied by 3, gives an answer of 18?

3 In an election 5090 votes were cast for the two candidates. Mr Wilson won by 260 votes. How many people voted for Wilson?

4 A 10p coin is 2 mm thick. Nicola has a pile of 10p coins which is 18·4 cm high. What is the value of the money in Nicola's pile of coins?

5 The school morning lasts 3 hours 30 minutes. How many 35-minute lessons are there?

6 Find two numbers which multiply together to give 24 and which add up to 10.

7 Mr and Mrs Webb cycle around a rectangular field which is 160 m long and 90 m wide. How far do they cycle, in km, if they complete 12 laps of the field?

8 When a certain number is divided by 20 the answer is 37. What is the number?

9 An aircraft takes $2\frac{3}{4}$ hours to complete a journey.
How long will the journey take if it travels at half the speed?

10 A garden 36 m long and 10 m wide is to be covered with peat, which is supplied in 60 kg sacks. 10 kg of peat covers an area of 20 m^2. How many sacks of peat are needed for the whole garden?

Homework 11F⊙

1 Find the result when two hundred and twelve thousand, five hundred and seven is added to sixty thousand, eight hundred and seventy.

2 Find the angle between the hands of a clock showing
   a 8:00 p.m.   **b** 11:00 a.m.

3 A badly typed three-digit number appears as 84★. Suki knows that the number is odd and divisible by 5. Find the number.

4 A car uses 9 litres of petrol for every 50 km travelled. Calculate the cost in £s of travelling 750 km if petrol costs 98p per litre.

5 Add together the 19th odd number and the 12th even number. (The first odd number is 1 and the first even number is 2.)

6 **a** Work out 8 × 125, without a calculator.
   b Use the result in part **a** to work out 12 000 ÷ 125.

7 A play was attended by 240 adults, each paying 80p, and 164 children, each paying 50p. How much in £s was paid altogether by the people attending the play?

8 The exchange rate in Spain is 1·5 euros to the £.
   a How many euros will I receive for £20?
   b A bottle of wine is priced at 4·80 euros. What is the equivalent cost in £s?

9 A pentomino is a set of five squares joined along their edges. See how many different pentominoes you can design on squared paper. Here are a few.

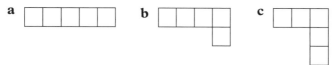

You may find that some of your designs are really the same, for example

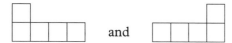

There are in fact 12 different pentominoes.

10 A man smokes 60 cigarettes a day and a packet of 20 costs £4·40.
   How much does he spend on cigarettes in a seven-day week?

Homework 11G

1 A suitcase is packed with 35 books, each weighing 420 g. The total weight of the suitcase and books is 17 kg. Find the weight of the suitcase.

2 Copy and complete.

 a 200 cm = ☐ m   b 2·3 m = ☐ cm   c 7·2 km = ☐ m

 d 0·8 m = ☐ cm   e 28 m = ☐ km   f 25 mm = ☐ cm

3 Maxine bought a car for £1200 and sold it six months later at a price 10% higher. At what price did she sell the car?

4 Copy and complete this pattern.

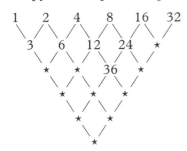

5 A box contains 200 assorted nails and screws and there are three times as many nails as screws.

 a How many screws are there?

 b What is the probability that an item chosen at random from the box will be a nail?

6 A 9-day holiday in Italy costs £170. Find the average cost per day, correct to the nearest pound.

7 Copy each statement and answer 'true' or 'false'.

 a $n + n = 2n$ b $3c - c = 3$ c $a + b = b + a$

 d $a - b = b - a$ e $n \times n^2 = n^3$ f $a \div 2 = \dfrac{2}{a}$

8 Mr Black's salary is £27 800 per year. He pays no tax on the first £5200 of his salary but pays 20% on the remainder. How much tax does he pay?

9 Petunia bought 20 plants at 85p each and a number of plants costing 45p each. In all she spent £22·40. How many of the less expensive plants did she buy?

10 ABCD is a square of side 10 cm.
   Side AB is increased by 30% to form rectangle AXYD.
   Calculate
   a the area of ABCD
   b the length BX
   c the area BXYC.

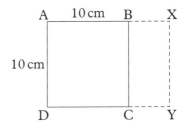

Homework 11H 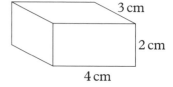○

1 A machine fills 690 oil drums in one hour. How many oil drums will it fill in 20 minutes?

2 Thirty books cost £75 and weigh 6000 g. Find
   a the cost and   **b** the weight of 12 of these books.

3 The entire surface area of this solid is covered with paint, the thickness of paint being 1 mm.
   a Find the total surface area of the solid.
   b Find the volume of paint used in m³.

4 The average length of Matt's pace is 70 cm. How many steps does Matt take in walking a distance of 350 m?

5 The moving pavement at an airway terminal goes at a speed of 0·8 m/s. If you are standing on the pavement, how far do you travel in
   a 10 s   **b** 1 minute   **c** 45 s?

6 Write these amounts correct to the nearest penny.
   a £5·638   **b** £0·721   **c** £11·655
   d £2·0725   **e** £8·111   **f** £7·077

7 The graph gives the charges made by Welwyn Motors for the hire of a van to travel various distances.

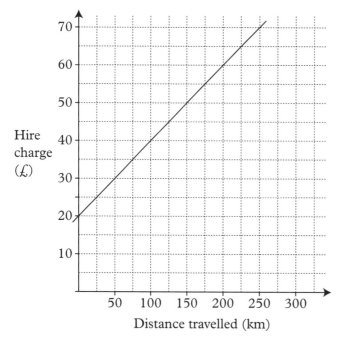

   a What is the hire charge for a van to travel 100 km?
   b What was the distance travelled by a van for which the hire charge was £70?

8 A number of tins of soup are packed in a box which weighs 2 kg. The total weight of the box and its contents is 19·5 kg. How many tins are in the box if each tin weighs 350 g?

9 A car dealer offers a discount of 5% when a car is paid for with cash.
   Find the cost of an £8000 car after the discount.

10 Which of these numbers
    6, 7, 8, 13, 15, 17, 23, 27, 39, 41, 54
    are
    a even   **b** divisible by 3
    c prime   **d** divisible by 9?

Homework 11I 🅲

Draw a copy of this crossnumber pattern. Find the answers using a calculator.
Where there are decimals put the point on the line between squares.

Across

1 $\sqrt{3136} \times 1.5$

2 $\sqrt{45\,678}$ (to 3 sf)

3 $191.1 \div 2.6$

5 $\dfrac{131 + 67}{7}$ (to 3 sf)

7 $766 + \sqrt{4761}$

9 30% of 1170

10 $152 - \sqrt{3481}$

11 $432 - (17 \times 22)$

12 $\dfrac{27.39}{2.14 - 2.074}$

14 80% of 650

16 37×3^3

17 $\dfrac{2.63}{1.41 \times 0.012}$ (to 3 sf)

Down

1 $47.2 \times 21.5 \times 0.86$ (to 3 sf)

4 $611 - (5.2 \times 5)$

6 7^3

8 π (to 4 sf)

9 $\dfrac{42}{2.4 - 1.3}$ (to 2 sf)

10 $120 - \sqrt{625}$

11 22% of 2450

13 $\dfrac{1}{0.0997^2}$ (to 3 sf)

14 $\dfrac{41}{7} + 0.0015$ (to 2 sf)

15 $\dfrac{\sqrt{169} \times 40}{8}$

Homework 11J

These diagrams show the number of squares along the diagonals
of three squares.

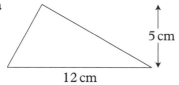

4 × 4

8 squares along
the diagonals

5 × 5

9 squares along
the diagonals

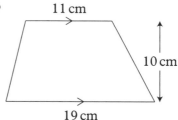

6 × 6

12 squares along
the diagonals

a Draw a similar diagram for a 7 × 7 square and count the squares along
the two diagonals.
b **Without** drawing diagrams, write the number of squares along the
diagonals of
   i   an 8 × 8 square
   ii a 13 × 13 square
   iii a 30 × 30 square.
c A square wall is covered by 400 square tiles.
   How many tiles are there along the two diagonals?

Homework 11K

1 Calculate the areas of these shapes.

a
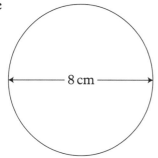
5 cm

12 cm

b 11 cm

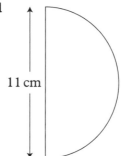

10 cm

19 cm

c

←——— 8 cm ———→

d

11 cm

2 Four people share 3 pizzas equally. How much pizza does each person have?

3 Look at this list of numbers.

112   37   637   44   1210   12   56   1102   65   370   4400   100

  a Write two numbers from the list where one number is ten times as big as the other number.

  b Find two numbers from the list which add up to 100.

  c Write a square number from the list.

4 A lift can carry up to 23 people. 311 people want to use the lift. How many times must it go up?

5 Chris is estimating the size of a room by counting his paces along each side.
He measures one pace and finds that it is 92 cm.

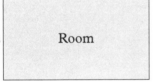

Work out the length and width of the room and give your answer in metres.

6 Andy is trying to find the square root of 12.
His calculator does not have a $\boxed{\sqrt{}}$ key.

1st   try 3×3 = 9
2nd   try 4×4 = 16
3rd   try $3·5 \times 3·5$ = 12·25

Make three more sensible trials to get as close as you can to $\sqrt{12}$.

7 Priya is working out 316×94.
She got an answer of 2970 but she thinks it may be wrong.

  a Make a rough estimate of 316×94.

  b Decide whether or not you think Priya got the answer right. Explain why.

Homework 11L

1 a Find 30% of £2000.
 b What percentage of £400 is the same as 20% of £800?

2 Five people are waiting to use the lift.
 They weigh
 71 kg, 82 kg, 47 kg, 92 kg and 65 kg.
 One kilogram is about 2·2 pounds.
 Can all five people use the lift at the same time?
 Show your working.

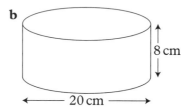

This lift can carry up to
700 pounds

3 Round 27 347 to
 a the nearest 10   **b** the nearest 100   **c** the nearest 1000.

4 A company built 40 houses each costing £90 000.
 What is the total cost of all 40 houses?

5 Calculate the volume of each solid.

a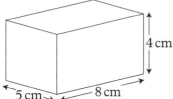

4 cm

5 cm   8 cm

b

8 cm

20 cm

6 a What is the name of an eight-sided shape?
 b 'All parallelograms have diagonals of equal length'.
   Is this statement true or false?
 c Name the shape which has three equal sides.

7 Write these numbers in order of size, smallest first.

 $4·2$ $\dfrac{3}{4}$ 2^2 -3 $0·6$ $\dfrac{1}{100}$

8 The totals for the rows and columns are given.
 Find the values of A, B, C and D.

A	C	B	D	43
C	C	C	C	44
D	C	B	B	35
B	D	C	A	43
43	43	36	43	

12   Examination style questions

Homework 12A

1 From the numbers in the cloud, write

 a the factors of 15

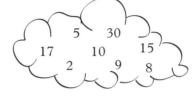

 b the multiples of 10

 c the square number

 d the prime numbers.

2 Work out the value of

 a $5m - n$ when $m = 6$ and $n = 2$

 b $3xy$ when $x = 10$ and $y = 9$

3 a Draw an accurate full-size drawing
   of the triangle.

 b Measure the size of angle C.

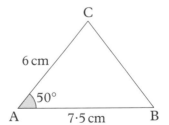

 c Work out the perimeter of the triangle.

4 Copy each statement and say whether it is true or false.
Give a reason for your answer.

a $7 + 8 + 12 = 12 + 8 + 7$

b $16 \div 4 = 4 \div 16$

c $3 \times 7 - 2 \times 4 = 7 + 6$

5 a Here is a list of numbers.

25   250   2500   25 000   250 000   2 500 000

Write the number which is

i a quarter of a million

ii two thousand, five hundred.

b Copy and complete

i $250 \times \square = 2\,500\,000$

ii $\square \div 100 = 25$

6 The sail on a boat has an area of $40\,\text{m}^2$.
An advertiser's logo covers 15% of the sail.
Work out the area of the sail.

7 Work out the answer to 216×27 without a calculator.

8 A number machine multiplies all numbers by 9 then subtracts 5.

In →→ ×9 →→ −5 →→ Out

a Copy and complete this table.

In	Out
6	49
3	
11	

b 175 came **out** of the machine. What number was put **in**?

c 6 came **out** of the machine. What number was put **in**?

9 a Copy this diagram and shade $\frac{2}{9}$ of it.

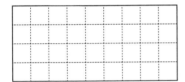

b What fraction of the shape below is shaded?

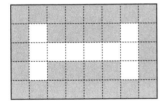

10 a Find the value of x.

b Find the value of y.

c Find the value of z.

Give a reason for your answer in each case.

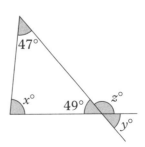

Homework 12B

1 a Work out $2^3 + 3^2$

b Work out $18 - 8 \div 2$

c Work out $12 - 4 \cdot 7$

2 Look at these five numbers 1, 2, 4, 7, 8

   a Which of these numbers are square numbers?

   b Which of these numbers are prime numbers?

   c Which of these numbers are factors of 20?

   d Write the largest 3-digit number you can make using
     3 different numbers.

   e Copy and complete the number square so that
     every row, column and diagonal adds up to 15.

6		
	5	9
	3	

3 Helen has a bag containing 11 beads. Four of them are white,
two are blue and the rest are yellow. One bead is taken at
random from the bag. Write the probability that it will be

   a blue   **b** yellow   **c** not yellow.

4 A company employs 48 people. The ratio of men to women in
this company is 3 : 5. How many employees are men?

5 Work out

a $\frac{2}{3}$ of $\frac{3}{5}$

b $\frac{5}{8} \times 10$

c $\frac{3}{4} - \frac{1}{6}$

6 Draw each shape and reflect it in the mirror line.

a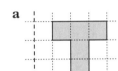

b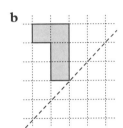

7 Copy and complete the table and then draw
the curve $y = x^2 + 1$. Draw axes like these.

x	−3	−2	−1	0	1	2	3
y							

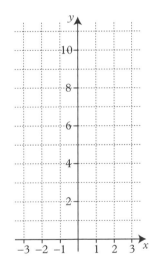

8 Solve these equations.

a $2n - 1 = 17$

b $3(x + 2) = 8$

c $4x - 3 = 2x + 7$

9 Seven people score these marks in a test.

28   30   34   35   41   43   97

a Find   **i** the mean mark

ii the median mark.

b Which average best describes these marks? Explain why.

10 The pie chart shows the favourite fruit chosen
in a survey of 480 people.
How many people chose

a lemon

b apple?

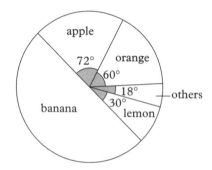

Homework 12C

1 Copy and complete this bill.

	Total
3 calculators at £7·95 each	_____
2 boxes of tape at £3·25 each	_____
20 m of electric cable at 60p per metre	_____
Total	_____

2 Simplify

a $5a - 2b + 7a + b$

b $4(3m - 2n)$

c $x(2x + 5)$

3 Tony has 5 cards. The 5 cards have a mean of 7, a median of 6 and a range of 12.
What are the five numbers on the cards?

4 Copy the grid and shape A.
   a Reflect shape A in the y-axis.
   Label the image B.

   b Rotate shape A 90° clockwise about
   the point (0, 0).
   Label the image C.

   c Translate the shape A with the vector $\begin{pmatrix} -3 \\ -7 \end{pmatrix}$.
   Label the image D.

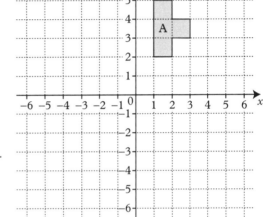

   d Reflect shape A in the line $y = x$.
   Label the image E.

5 Jerome looked up the weather records for his area
over the previous five years. He worked out that
the probability that it will rain on any day in April is 0·3.

   a Find the probability that it will not rain
   on my birthday (April 23rd).

   b On how many days would you expect
   it to rain in April?

April 2007			
	5	12	19	26
	6	13	20	27
	7	14	21	28
1	8	15	22	29
2	9	16	23	30
3	10	17	24
4	11	18	25

6 Solve these equations.

 a $3x - 7 = 11$

 b $3(x - 2) = 9$

 c $\frac{x}{7} = 12$

7 Use a calculator to work these out, giving your answers to 1 dp.

 a $8 \cdot 2^3 + \sqrt{98 \cdot 5 - 11}$

 b $\dfrac{31 \cdot 78 - 19 \cdot 2}{0 \cdot 714}$

8 Work out
 a the bearing of A from B

 b the bearing of B from A.

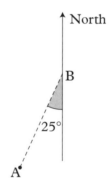

9 a Use Pythagoras' theorem to find
  the height of the triangle shown.

 b Work out the area of the triangle,
  giving your answer to 1 dp.

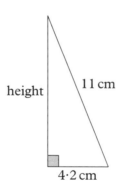

10 a The distance between Paris and Rouen is about 80 km. Work out an estimate for the distance in miles.

b A computer weighs 4 kg. Work out an estimate for the weight in pounds.

Homework 12D

1 Use the graph to find solutions to these simultaneous equations.

a $2x - y = 4$
   $x + y = 8$

b $x - 2y = -10$
   $2x - y = 4$

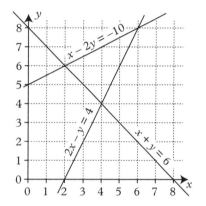

2 From the stem-and-leaf diagram, work out

a the median

b the mode

c the range.

stem	leaf
2	1 3 7
3	2 3 8 9
4	3 8 9
5	0 8 8 8
6	1 5 9

Key 6|1 = 61

3 a Find the area of a circle of radius 4 cm.
Give your answer correct to 2 dp.

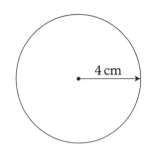

b Find the volume of the cylinder shown.
Give your answer correct to 1 dp.

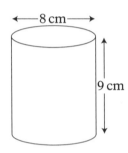

4 An isosceles triangle has sides of length 8 cm, 8 cm and 6 cm.
Find the area of the triangle.

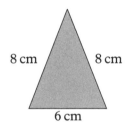

5 Michelle has two spinners. She spins
both spinners and multiplies the
numbers obtained. For example
a '2' and a '4' give 8.

a Copy and complete the grid to
show all the possible outcomes.

b Find the probability of getting an
answer of 4 when the numbers
are multiplied together.

×	1	2	3	4
1				
2				8
3				
4				

6 a Use a ruler and a protractor to
   draw this triangle accurately

   b Measure and write the
   length of side marked x.

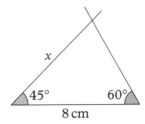

7 A machine fills bags of flour.
   The weight of each bag of flour is 620 g, correct to the nearest 10 g.
   Between what limits does the actual weight lie?

8 Joe left home at 09:00 and cycled to a
   friend's house. He stayed there for half
   an hour and then returned home.
   The graph shows his journey.

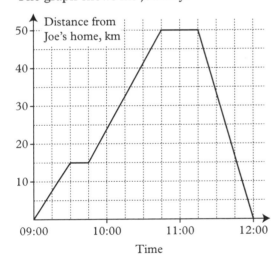

a When did he arrive at his friend's house?

b At what speed did he cycle for the first half an hour?

c At what speed did he cycle home?

d What happened at 09:30?

9 a Make x the subject of the formula

$ax + t = m$

b Make x the subject of the formula

$\dfrac{mx}{c} = d$

10 Solve these inequalities.

a $x + 7 > 10$

b $4x - 1 < 19$

c $2x + 1 \geqslant x + 7$

11 a Write these numbers in standard form.

i $40\,000$ **ii** $0{\cdot}007$

b Work out and write each answer in index form.

i $4^3 \times 4^6$ **ii** $7^8 \div 7^2$

c Simplify the expression

$\dfrac{n^{10} \times n^7}{n^5}$

Homework 12E

1 Use a protractor to measure the bearing of

a Nalton from Exham

b Exham from Nalton.

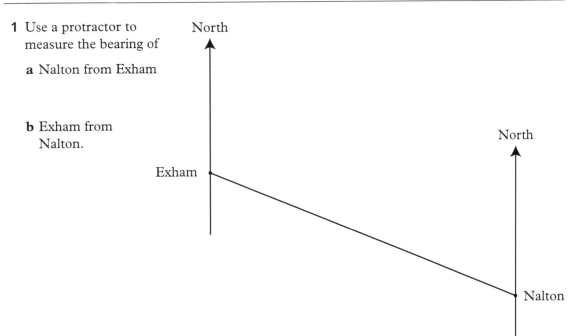

North

Exham

North

Nalton

2 In the diagram AD = 7 cm, AC = 11 cm and DB = 5 cm.
Angles ∠ADC and ∠CDB are right angles.
Calculate the length of CB.
Give your answer correct to 1 dp.

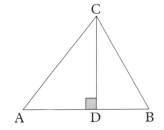

3 A rectangular tank has a length of 6 m and a width of 3 m.
How high is the tank if its capacity is 27 000 litres?

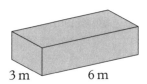

3 m   6 m

4 a Use a calculator to work out these, giving your answers to 1 dp.

    i $(4\cdot2)^3 - \dfrac{22\cdot7}{0\cdot52}$ **ii** $\sqrt{\dfrac{109\cdot63}{1\cdot6 - 0\cdot782}}$

  b Work these out, giving your answers in standard form.

    i $(7 \times 10^8) \times (5 \times 10^7)$ **ii** $(8\cdot2 \times 10^5) \div (2 \times 10^{-2})$

5 The diagram shows a cuboid.
Point A has coordinates $(0, 3, 4)$.
Write the coordinates of

  a C   **b** G   **c** D

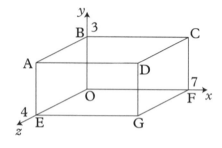

6 £4500 is invested in a bank at 5% per annum compound interest.
How much money will there be after 3 years?

7 The diagram shows a rectangle.
Find the value of x and hence calculate
the perimeter of the rectangle.

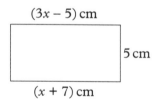

8 The diagram shows a prism.
Calculate the volume of the prism.

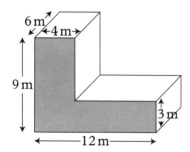

9 A bag contains a number of balls coloured red, green, yellow and blue.
The table shows the probability of selecting a ball of each colour.

red	green	yellow	blue
0·15		0·4	0·2

a What is the probability of selecting a green ball?

b What is the probability of selecting a ball which is **not** blue?

c Karen selects a ball and then replaces it. She does this 200 times.
How many times would you expect her to select a red ball?

10 The area of the rectangle shown is 73 cm^2.
Use trial and improvement to find x to one
decimal place.
You must show your working.

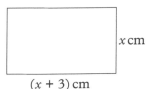

x cm

$(x + 3)$ cm

Homework 12F

1 The mean weight of 11 people is 61 kg.

a Work out the total weight of all 11 people.

b One person of weight 49 kg leaves the group.
Work out the mean weight of the remaining people.

2 Copy and complete the table and then draw the curve
$y = x^2 + 2x$.

x	−3	−2	−1	0	1	2	3
x²						4	
+2x						4	
y						8	

3 Sumithra is thinking of a number. When she adds 7 to the number and
then multiplies the result by 3, the answer is 18.
Let x be the number which Sumithra is thinking of.
Form an equation involving x and then solve it to find
Sumithra's number.

4 Copy the diagram on to square grid paper and
then draw the enlargement of the shape
with scale factor 2 and centre of enlargement O.

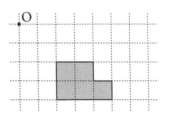

5 Lines AB and CD are parallel.

a Find angle PRC.

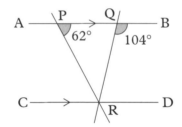

b Find angle QRD.

c Find angle PRQ.

6 Wayne bought a car for £6400.
He later sold it for £5440.
Calculate the loss he made as a percentage of the price
he paid for the car.

7 A window is in the shape of a rectangle
joined to a semicircle.
Calculate the area of the window.
Give your answer correct to 1 dp.

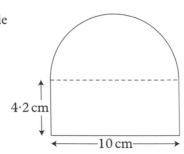